# FAMOUS PHYSICISTS

# FAMOUS PHYSICISTS

A. L. MANN and A. C. VIVIAN

*Illustrated by*
NORMA OST

THE JOHN DAY COMPANY
NEW YORK

# AUTHOR'S NOTE

THIS book contains the life histories of a number of dedicated men. All are early scientists who dealt with problems of physical laws, and whose vision and labor laid the foundations for the scientific advances already achieved in our modern world — and for the breathtaking possibilities of the future.

As will be seen from the pages that follow, much of the greatness of these early physicists was due to their refusal to accept any theory or teaching which was not in accord with observation and experiment. It is, indeed, this persistent searching after the truth that makes the history of their lives of special interest and value for us.

At the conclusion of each biography, the reader is shown (with simple text and diagram) how to undertake experiments which follow along lines similar to those taken by these early pioneers of science. The authors believe that this is a particularly useful feature of the book, since not only will it help the reader to have a more complete understanding of the actual work of the scientists themselves, but it will also provide a practical grounding in elementary physics, which will be of special value to those who have not followed a regular course in the subject.

A.L.M.
A.C.V.

# CONTENTS

I never yet found a child who was not able to understand by simple explanation, and to enjoy the point of an experiment.

— MICHAEL FARADAY

# FAMOUS PHYSICISTS

# CHAPTER I

# ARCHIMEDES (287–212 B.C.)

WHEN we think of those people who deserve the title physicists it is difficult to realize that one of the greatest of these was born 287 years before Jesus Christ. That man was Archimedes of Syracuse, the son of Pheidias, a geometer and astronomer.

When next you see a man toiling with a crowbar or lever to accomplish work which his unaided bodily strength could not achieve, remember Archimedes, for it was he who first fully noted the principles of leverage. The next time you handle a football, imagine you have been asked to find out its exact volume without any previous mathematical formula to help you —

Archimedes dealt successfully with this and similar problems well over two thousand years ago. Supposing a rich relative gave you a gold coin, could you make quite certain that it was really gold and not made of a baser metal? Archimedes could have told you.

Even today, many of his inventions are in general use. His teachings were the foundation of so much of our scientific thought that we often apply principles which he discovered, without appreciating their source.

Part of Archimedes' education occurred at Alexandria, and after his return to his native Syracuse in Sicily he corresponded regularly with students of geometry there. In Archimedes' day, Syracuse had defeated Athens in war and had colonized various parts of Sicily. The city was then some 500 years old and during this time had seen a succession of rulers good and bad. Hiero — the king of Syracuse when Archimedes was alive — proved a wise ruler who encouraged learning and generally sought to improve the lot of his people.

It was largely at King Hiero's insistence that Archimedes put so many of his discoveries in pure science to practical use. The wise ruler thought highly of this man of science, although he could not always understand his work. There came a time when the king chal-

lenged him to set aside his abstract studies and produce more practical benefits for his fellow citizens.

Archimedes disliked any practical application of his work, thinking all such results were amusing tricks of construction that had little significance against the many weighty mathematical formulae upon which he was engaged. But King Heiro would have no excuses. He commanded his "wise man" to produce tangible results for the benefit of the community. Archimedes promptly answered that if he could but have another planet to stand upon, he would produce sufficient force to move the earth.

Hiero was skeptical and demanded proof of such an astonishing boast. Archimedes accordingly arranged for one of the king's galleys to be hauled ashore. And this having been done with much effort and labor, he then caused the ship to be loaded with cargo and by an ingenious arrangement of ropes and pulleys, coupled to what we now imagine to have been a form of windlass, drew the laden ship toward himself single-handed.

Hiero was both amazed and delighted by such a remarkable feat. Sending for Archimedes, he privately pleaded with him to turn his talents to the invention of engines of war for the defense of the city. At that time there was beginning a struggle between Carthage and Rome for possession of Sicily, and although Syracuse would favor first one power and then the other, the wise king guessed that should the struggle ever ripen into war, his fair city would be menaced.

Obediently, Archimedes devoted much thought and time to the application of his mathematical and scientific discoveries, and the good citizens of Syracuse marveled at the strange new machines which he produced both for war and for peace. For himself, he would have been much more content to have been left undisturbed to his studies. Indeed, so immersed was he with his work that his friends had to remind him of meals and forcibly carry him off to the baths to ensure his rest and recreation.

Even at the baths, Archimedes would not leave his beloved geometry. While his friends anointed him with oil he woud reach down and dip his fingers in the sand and proceed to draw involved problems upon his own body. It was while he was actually bathing that he made one of his most famous discoveries. King Hiero, as an offering to his gods, had ordered a golden crown to be made, but upon receiving it from his goldsmiths had suspicions that it was, in fact, not pure gold.

Apparently, the king's craftsmen were not above cheating their master, and Hiero became so worried by the thought of offering his gods something less than pure gold that he commanded the services of Archimedes. The learned physicist was still puzzled by this unusual problem when his friends came to carry him to the baths. As he stepped into the water, he noticed that some overflowed over the sides of the bath; the more of his body he submerged, the more water he displaced.

This is a common enough occurrence in any age, but it took the genius of Archimedes to recognize it for its true value to science. So excited was he with his discovery that he leaped from his bath and ran naked through the streets of the town shouting, "Eureka! Eureka! (I have found it!)"

In the moment of taking his bath he had discovered that any given body plunged into fluid will displace a volume of fluid equal to its own volume. Later, he took a known weight of proven gold, lowered it into a vessel of water, and measured its displacement. Armed with this knowledge, he had only to weigh the crown in air and find its volume by immersing it in water, to be able to discover whether it contained only pure gold. Actually, it is recorded that the crown did, in fact, contain a baser metal and we can only assume that Hiero took appropriate measures with his goldsmiths.

For Archimedes it was just another problem solved, and he turned to other things. Having found and demonstrated the powers of pulleys and levers, he invented the water screw or screw pump. Every time an endless screw is used in machinery, large or small, we have to thank Archimedes. Every designer of ships, cars and airplanes must at some time have recourse to mathematical laws which he first discovered.

The sum total of Archimedes' work is diverse and of such volume that one understands how his friends could forgive him the forgetfulness and eccentricity he is said to have shown. During his lifetime he wrote many books dealing with subjects such as spheres, circles, spirals, gravity, floating bodies, levers and pulleys. Little had been done on these subjects before his time. Unfortunately, at least six of his books were lost and the priceless knowledge they contained had to be rediscovered by other men in later times.

Having satisfied King Hiero with the various machines for peace and war which he had produced for him, Archimedes again turned to his studies and had soon progressed so far in the field of mathematics that he could work out the number of grains of sand it would require to fill a sphere equal in radius to the supposed distance between the earth and the stars.

Then he experimented with a scale beam and, finding that the short side of the beam needed a much heavier weight than the long side to produce balance, he set to work and revealed the reason for this by mathematics, and through this discovery was enabled to carry out some remarkable research into the center of gravity of various geometric forms.

Archimedes continued quietly in this manner until King Hiero died in 215 B.C. By now, the second Punic War was being fought. During his reign, Hiero had allied himself to Rome, supplying her with men and money. After the king's death, friends of Hannibal, encouraged by the latter's crossing of the Alps into Italy, succeeded in persuading Syracuse to break off the alliance with Rome and to join forces with Carthage.

Rome's reply to this sudden change of loyalties was to send an expedition under Marcellus to besiege the city both by land and by sea. And now Hiero's former insistence that Archimedes should produce some practical results from his studies greatly aided Syracuse in its endeavors to fight off the Roman army and navy which beset it.

Archimedes was soon to see how powerful the "toys" of his mathematical genius could be. The Roman soldiers, advancing against the landward defenses of Syracuse, were first amazed and then terror-stricken to see huge catapults whip silently above the city walls and hurl huge stones, molten lead, spears and other missiles at them with such force and deadly precision that they broke ranks and retreated in disorder.

On the seaward side of the city the Roman navy was receiving an even more alarming display of Archimedes' ingenuity. Large machines of war released massive beams which fell end on, sinking any vessel they struck. Huge iron grappling hooks suddenly descended upon vessels and either lifted them bodily into the air and released them so that they plunged below the surface with their crews, or else spun them about with such force that they were dashed to pieces on the rocks below the city.

Such terror and confusion were created in the ranks of his soldiers and sailors that Marcellus judged it wiser to call off any direct assault on the city and, instead, sought to defeat it by siege. For three years, Roman forces ringed Syracuse by land and sea — always ensuring that they were a safe distance from the many marvelous machines that Archimedes had made.

Aware that his machines had saved his city from the Romans for at least a time, Archimedes returned once again to his studies. By now his name had become legend, not only to his fellow citizens of Syracuse, but also of the Romans who ringed the city. In fact, so impressed had Marcellus been by the terrible new weapons that had been arraigned against him that he gave orders that their inventor was to be taken alive, so that he could learn more of this scholar whose genius had withstood the might of Roman legions and galleys.

No doubt the citizens of Syracuse hoped that Marcellus would become impatient and finally withdraw his forces. But although he would not again expose his men to the armaments which defended the city, the Roman commander realized that by cutting off all supplies from the city he must eventually starve it into submission — and even Archimedes' mathematical knowledge could not defeat him in this purpose.

How the great scientist managed during the years of siege is not recorded. Presumably, he was so deep in his studies that he scarcely noticed the altered conditions. Then came the day when the Romans, helped by sympathizers within the city, finally pierced the defenses and carried their swords through the streets of Syracuse.

Unaware of the Romans' triumph, Archimedes sat in his room busy with problems worked out diagrammatically in the sand of the floor. When Roman soldiers burst in upon him, he angrily bade them not to step on his diagrams. Unaware that he was in the presence of the man whom their commander had ordered to be taken alive, one of the soldiers drew his sword and killed Archimedes.

Even the Romans were appalled by the death of one so learned, and Marcellus freely gave permission for the friends of Archimedes to bury him. A sculptured cylinder and a sphere were chosen as his monument, and a short verse testified that Archimedes regarded as his own greatest achievement the proving of the mutual proportions of these two bodies.

As the power of Syracuse waned the city was deserted and finally fell into ruins. Archimedes' grave was forgotten until the great orator and philosopher Cicero, wandering the rubble-strewn streets more than a century later, came upon the tomb and realized that he had found the burial place of one of the cleverest men that the world had known.

It is typical of Archimedes that in none of his writings is there mention of the many machines for war and peace with which he delighted King Hiero. Knowledge of these were handed down to us by other writers of his day. His own books contain the calculations and formulae of those many mathematical laws which are the foundation of our physical knowledge.

## EXPERIMENTS

### WEIGHING MACHINE (ROMAN STEELYARD)

As WE have seen, Archimedes' discoveries ranged over a wide field of physical laws. We have chosen two simple experiments to demonstrate just a fraction of the work which he encompassed in his lifetime.

First, we will use his knowledge of the law of levers to produce a weighing machine similar to the one with which he experimented.

He found that when a lever, resting upon a support about which it can turn, is perfectly balanced, the weight(s) times the distance from the support on the left-hand side is exactly equal to the weight(s) times the distance from the support on the right-hand side. When talking about levers we call the support the *Fulcrum*; the force to be moved is the *Load*; the force that balances or moves the *Load* is the *Power* or *Effort*.

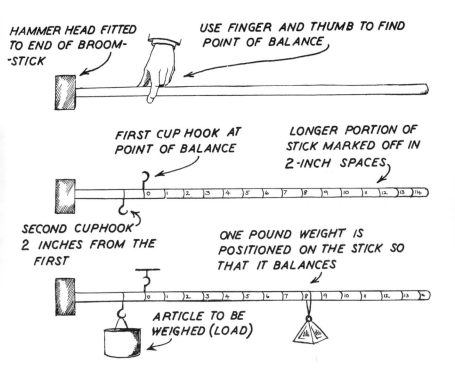

HAMMER HEAD FITTED TO END OF BROOM--STICK

USE FINGER AND THUMB TO FIND POINT OF BALANCE

FIRST CUP HOOK AT POINT OF BALANCE

LONGER PORTION OF STICK MARKED OFF IN 2-INCH SPACES

SECOND CUPHOOK 2 INCHES FROM THE FIRST

ONE POUND WEIGHT IS POSITIONED ON THE STICK SO THAT IT BALANCES

ARTICLE TO BE WEIGHED (LOAD)

YOU WILL NEED: A broomstick; the head of a hammer or ax weighing about 2 to 3 pounds that can be fixed to one end of the stick; two cup hooks; a 1-pound weight.

First, fix the hammer head to one end of the broomstick. Then hold the stick suspended between the fingers and thumb until you have found the point of balance. This will probably be from 4 inches to 12 inches from the hammer head.

Now screw a cup hook exactly into the point of balance so that the stick will assume a horizontal position when suspended from a piece of string. The second cup hook must be screwed into the opposite side of the stick at a point two inches from the point of balance and along the weighted side of the stick.

Starting from the Fulcrum (point of balance) mark the longer portion of the stick off in two-inch spaces. When this has been completed you are ready to put your weighing machine to work.

Suspend the broomstick from its point of balance and attach the object to be weighed to the second hook. Tie a loop of string around the one-pound weight and slip it over the free end of the stick. Slide the weight along until the broomstick is once more balanced.

A simple math problem will now provide us with the weight of the Load:

Load × Distance from Fulcrum = Effort × Distance from Fulcrum.

Therefore the Load × one space = 1 lb. × 8½ spaces.

Therefore Load = 8½.

Which means that the can being weighed in the accompanying diagram weighs 8½ pounds.

This lever balance, as our weighing machine is called, was actually used by early shopkeepers to weigh their provisions, while improved versions are still in use where sacks of grain or carcasses of meat have to be weighed.

### THE MODEL DIVER

For this second experiment in the field of Archimedes' discov-

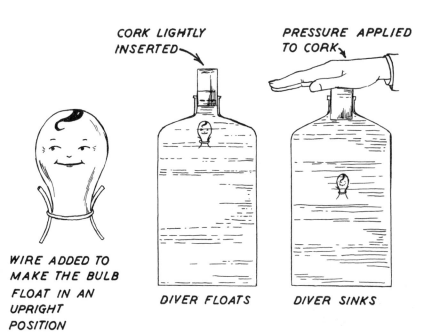

CORK LIGHTLY INSERTED

PRESSURE APPLIED TO CORK

WIRE ADDED TO MAKE THE BULB FLOAT IN AN UPRIGHT POSITION

DIVER FLOATS

DIVER SINKS

eries we will have recourse to one of the lessons he learned when he immersed himself in his bath and noticed the displacement of water which took place.

He subsequently found that when objects were weighed in fluid they weighed less than they did in air, the loss of weight being equal to the weight of fluid displaced by the object.

e.g.   Weight of a stone in air $= 10$ lb.

Weight of a stone in water $= 7\frac{1}{2}$ lb.

Therefore weight of water displaced $= 2\frac{1}{2}$ lb.

# FAMOUS PHYSICISTS

If the object's bulk pushes aside the same, or a greater weight of fluid than its own weight, the object will float.

YOU WILL NEED: The small rubber bulb from an eyedropper; a bottle filled with water; a cork.

Remove the rubber bulb from an eyedropper and put it into a bottle filled to the top with water. The open end of the bulb should be pointing downward. If it tends to float sideways or turn upside down, weight the bottom by adding small pieces of wire pierced through the rim of the bulb until it floats in the desired position.

If you want to amuse and mystify a younger brother or sister, a comical face can be painted on the rubber bulb.

Make sure that the bottle is quite full of water and then place a cork in the bottleneck. Press gently down on the cork and the diver will descend; when the pressure is relaxed the diver will return to the top of the bottle again.

The diver sinks because the pressure of the water transmits pressure to the rubber bulb and makes it slightly smaller. The diver no longer displaces as much water as before and the upthrust is less than the diver's weight, therefore it sinks to the bottom. When the pressure is released, the diver resumes its former shape and floats again.

# CHAPTER II

# ROGER BACON (1214–1294)

ROGER BACON was one of the earliest pioneers in science. Born in Ilchester, Somerset, in 1214, he is now considered as something of a wonder man of the Middle Ages. If ever a man was born out of his time, that one was certainly Roger Bacon. His keen brain and persistent pursuit after knowledge earned him the title of magician from his ignorant contemporaries — and he was punished accordingly.

His family fared badly in the troublesome times of Henry III, but although they suffered great financial loss there remained sufficient estate to support Roger and some brothers at Oxford.

At quite an early age, young Roger showed an intensely religious turn of mind, taking holy orders at Oxford before he had reached manhood, although it was not until he was thirty-five years of age that he joined the Franciscan Order and became a friar.

After leaving Oxford he studied and taught in Paris, which was then the intellectual center of Europe. It was in this city that he took his degree as doctor of divinity, and in these early days his fame as a teacher earned for him the title: "the Admirable Doctor."

These were still formative years for Roger Bacon. With so much knowledge to be encompassed, he applied himself diligently to his education. He spent £2,000 on books and scientific instruments, an amount possibly equal to some $85,000 by today's standards.

He was soon far in advance of the scholars of his day. Having mastered Greek, Arabic and Hebrew, he was able to read important books in their original tongues, and uncovered knowledge which had hitherto lain dormant. Ever a seeker after truth, he believed there was as much to be discovered through practical experiment as through blindly accepting the writings of Aristotle and other great philosophers of the past.

It was this refusal to accept knowledge at second

hand, without proving the truth of what had been previously taught, which was to bring him into such grave trouble with the Church of his day. Aware through his own translations and experiments that much that was being taught was, in fact, false, Roger Bacon showed his contempt for the shallow, insincere scholars who sought to limit his quest for knowledge.

He returned to Oxford, by now a friar of the Franciscan Order, and soon, in defiance of religious authority, was leading a new school of thought. Still studying and learning himself, his brilliant personality found kindred noncomformists, fired with enthusiasm by his experimental ventures into mathematics, chemistry and physics.

He convinced his students that either the findings of formerly revered wise men had been misinterpreted through faulty translation, or the scholars themselves had been incorrect in some of their conclusions. It followed that for one or the other reason much conventional knowledge was spurious.

Ever striving after truth, Friar Bacon's quest sent him ranging over the whole field of human thought, and with his unrivaled mind he diligently pursued studies that were centuries in advance of his time.

# ROGER BACON (1214-1294)

He knew something of gunpowder and the magnetic needle; his experiments with light led to his invention of the magnifying glass, and through this to the corrective lenses for spectacles.

It was his insight into natural laws which was really instrumental in Christopher Columbus's sailing west in search of another sea route to the Indies. Two centuries before Columbus's time, Roger Bacon believed that the world was round. This belief was discovered in his writing by Pierre d'Ailly, who published the finding, much later, under his own name. Columbus, in his turn, read d'Ailly. Perhaps this inspired the idea that led to the discovery of the New World.

It was typical of the gross obscurity of medieval thought that, although Roger Bacon brought to light so many important discoveries of true scientific value, he also floundered among the superstitious notions of his age. He believed in the philosopher's stone and the elixir of life, and although his work led him to realize that mathematics must be the true foundation for astronomy, he also believed in astrology as a means of prophetic vision.

By now, he was in grave disrepute with authority. His refusal to accept conventional teachings, the brilliance and enthusiasm which brought him such loyal followers were all frowned upon. We had not yet reached an age when we burned our heretics at the stake, but severe punishment was not unknown, and already the titles of "magician," "sorcerer," and "man-of-the-devil" were being whispered about Friar Bacon.

As news of some of his more startling experiments leaked out, the Franciscans became more and more perturbed at the thought of one of their number being in league with the devil. Finally, they could tolerate his teachings no longer and he was banished to virtual imprisonment in Paris. Here, for ten years, he was forbidden to write or have free conversation. For a whole decade he was kept away from his beloved books and instruments, and there is little doubt that a lesser man might well have succumbed to such intellectual torment.

Fortunately, Roger Bacon contrived to sustain both life and sanity during his detention in Paris. The rich harvest of knowledge gleaned from his studies was not to be lost to mankind.

His one influential friend was a papal legate, Guy de Foulques, in England. In 1265, this friend was elected Pope. A man of vision himself, the new Pope told

Bacon to ignore the Franciscan authority, bidding him to put into writing the thoughts and theories which his superiors maintained were false. He assured the unhappy prisoner that he would then take the matter up himself.

Until then, Roger Bacon had written only a few learned essays, but with Pope Clement's encouragement he began an astonishing feat of writing. Without reference to books, and without the stimulus of conversation with other scholars, he brought his whole fiery zeal to bear, not so much to vindicate himself as to prove the truth of his discoveries, that others might be encouraged to ignore the narrow beliefs and teachings of his day.

In less than 18 months he wrote three lengthy books: *Opus Majus,* in which he set down his ideas in relation to mankind, religion, philosophy and science; *Opus Minus,* a shortened version of the first volume, written in case *Opus Majus* failed to reach the Pope; and *Opus Tertium,* a remarkable introduction to the first two volumes. Together, the three books made up some 1,340 pages in which Bacon gave rein to his genius in reviewing the whole sphere of human knowledge.

We have no way of knowing how much of his writings actually reached Pope Clement. It is, in fact, doubtful whether Roger Bacon had had time to complete his works before the Pope became seriously ill. His books did obtain his release from prison, but when Pope Clement died, the friar was again imprisoned by those who saw in his writings and teachings danger to their own positions.

Pope Clement died in 1268 and it was not until the year 1292 that Roger Bacon was again released. Jerome of Ascoli, head of the Franciscan Order, had been responsible for consigning the friar to captivity again. When Jerome eventually became Pope himself, Roger Bacon wrote him a sympathetic document acquainting him with the best means of avoiding the infirmities of old age. We do not know whether it was gratitude for the information, or a matter of uneasy conscience for the wrong that he had done the peerless scholar, which prompted the new Pope to order his final release.

By now an old man, nearing the end of his days, Roger Bacon returned to Oxford. It was here that conformist authority had first dealt harshly with him, yet it held also many happier memories of his youth. But he was to enjoy only two years of freedom, dying in his eightieth year in 1294.

## ROGER BACON (1214-1294)

To the last he was hated and feared by those who misguidedly saw him as a sorcerer and heretic. But with Pope Clement's help, his life had not been wasted. The findings of a lifetime's brilliant study and research were now committed to writing — although these same works were locked away from common knowledge for many years.

Centuries later, scholars discovered his work, and little by little his teachings began to bear fruit. They marveled that such genius had flourished so long before their time, without acknowledgment.

His books showed Roger Bacon to be the first of our true scientists, one whose unflagging search for truth made him seek cause and effect through practical experiment. Had his contemporaries been prepared to accept his teachings, there is little doubt that scientific learning would have received a much earlier impetus.

In an age of almost complete ignorance of physical laws and science, the friar experimented with light and lenses until he had produced the first magnifying glass. His writings also revealed that he acquired sufficient knowledge of the laws of optics to reveal the properties of the microscope and the telescope. Indeed, some believe that he made a primitive form of the latter in-

37

strument, which was to revolutionize our knowledge of astronomy.

Mention has already been made of the friar's belief that the world was round and not flat, as then popularly supposed. It required two further centuries of knowledge, and the tenacity of purpose of Christopher Columbus, before this finding had its dramatic outcome.

We also know that Roger Bacon discovered and experimented with gunpowder. And in an England that was still held in the thrall of ignorance and superstition, his keen, prophetic mind foresaw the use of steam as a motive power by land and sea, as well as the practical possibility of balloons, diving bells, and suspension bridges. Indeed, how a man born into such an era of credulous thought could have had such vision and, moreover, the requisite courage to adhere to his beliefs in the face of such arrogant and harsh injustice, is hard to imagine.

England of the thirteenth century did not readily accept scholars, certainly none of the intellect of Roger Bacon, with his teachings and messages that were hundreds of years ahead of his time. He was fortunate, perhaps, in escaping a martyr's death at the stake. But imprisonment was cruel enough for one who sought only truth and freedom.

Today, with our precise scientific instruments and machine-ground lenses, it is easy enough for our scientists to surpass Roger Bacon's findings. Following, however, are two simple experiments, using easily obtainable equipment, which will provide us with the type of practical discovery which the learned friar must have made.

## EXPERIMENTS

### THE CANDLE AND THE JAR OF WATER

WHEN an object is reflected in a mirror, the image produced seems as far behind the mirror as the object is in front of it. Try standing about two feet in front of a mirror and you will note how your reflection will appear to be two feet "behind" the mirror.

We can use this and the fact that a plain piece of glass will reflect light as well as allow us to see through it, to create the illusion of a candle burning under water.

YOU WILL NEED: Stub of candle; large jar of water, sheet of glass; sheet of cardboard.

First, support a pane of clear glass in an upright position and place a lighted stub of candle about 9 inches in front of the glass.

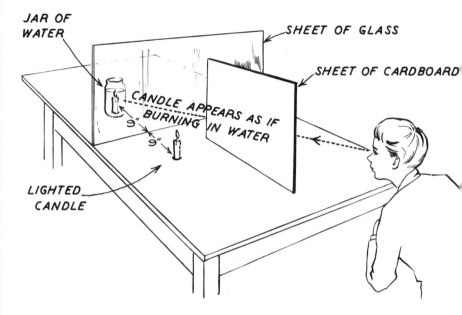

JAR OF WATER

SHEET OF GLASS

SHEET OF CARDBOARD

CANDLE APPEARS AS IF BURNING IN WATER

3"

3"

LIGHTED CANDLE

On the opposite side of the glass place a jar of water. If the jar is viewed through the glass from the candle side, it can be moved around until the reflection of the burning candle appears to stand inside the jar of water. Measure the distance between the jar and the glass and it will be found to equal the distance between the glass and the candle.

To mystify your friends (and produce the magical effect which would have worried many scholars in Roger Bacon's day) arrange a screen of cardboard to hide the candle from the viewer, as shown in the diagram. To anyone with little knowledge of physical laws, it will now appear as though you have managed to light a candle and keep it burning inside a jar of water.

BRIGHT LIGHT

SHEET OF GLASS

BLACK PAINTED
BOARD OR WOOD

REFLECTED
PICTURE
LATERALLY
INVERTED

PICTURE TO BE COPIED

### THE GRAPHOSCOPE

A GRAPHOSCOPE is an apparatus for copying pictures exactly. It uses the same facts as the candle-and-jar experiment; i.e., clear glass can be seen through and acts as a mirror, and the reflection of an object appears as far behind a mirror as the object is in front of it.

Unfortunately, a mirror reflects things back to front. This must be taken into account when copying our pictures.

YOU WILL NEED: Black-painted cardboard or wood; sheet of glass; bright light; pencil; drawing paper; picture to copy.

41

# FAMOUS PHYSICISTS

Stand a black-painted sheet of cardboard or wood upright, and a sheet of clear glass at right angles to it, halfway along its length (see diagram).

Place the picture to be copied on one side of the glass and a sheet of drawing paper on the opposite side. Now arrange an electric bulb or a reading lamp, etc. so that the picture is very brightly lit.

By looking through the glass at the plain sheet of drawing paper, the reflection of your picture will be seen. This can be copied by drawing along the lines as reflected. The picture will be back to front, but if a sheet of carbon paper is placed face upward under the drawing paper, the carbon copy on the reverse side of the paper will be the correct way about.

This experiment is best performed when the sole source of illumination is the bright light above the picture.

# CHAPTER III

# GALILEO (1564–1642)

THE young man noted with satisfaction that many people had gathered that morning around the great leaning tower in Pisa. He recognized various students and professors from his university as well as some of the more prominent townsfolk.

He smiled to himself as he shifted the weight of several iron balls more comfortably in his arms. It would not be easy to climb the numerous stairs to the top of the tower, but the labor would be worthwhile. He knew that his forthcoming experiment would shatter old beliefs and show the world a great new truth.

He was breathing heavily by the time he had reached

the top of the curiously tilted eight-story tower. Carefully placing his simple equipment at his feet, he looked down at his audience below and announced that he would drop balls of different weight, two at a time, and asked that they should listen for the sound of the balls striking the ground.

Taking up the first two balls — one large and the other small — he held them at arm's length over the side of the tower. He was standing at that point at the top of the building which overhung the base by some 14 feet. When he released the balls they fell, without interruption, to the ground below.

The people gathered below listened keenly and heard but a single sound as both balls struck the ground at the same time. There were many of them who failed to realize the significance of this comparatively simple experiment, even after the young man at the top of the tower had repeated it several times for their benefit. But his students and colleagues were aware of the importance of his discovery.

Galileo Galilei had proved the Greek philosopher, Aristotle, wrong  He had shown them, by means of a simple experiment that any one of them could have made, that no matter what difference there may be in

the weight of two falling bodies, they both travel at the same speed.

Aristotle, one-time tutor of Alexander the Great, and one of the world's earliest great thinkers, claimed that if two objects of different weight were dropped, the heavier body would travel at a proportionately greater speed. And for almost 2,000 years everyone had accepted this ancient teaching without further thought. Galileo was the first man to have discounted this theory in favor of actual experiment — with the result that we have already seen.

Not that Galileo earned any popularity by proving the truth of his own theory. Those scholars and philosophers who had been blindly following the teachings of Aristotle were furious that a mere nobody such as this young upstart should have set out to show them that only those reasonings which could be supported by proof had the right to be accepted as truth.

So many enemies did Galileo make as the result of this experiment that feeling was running high against him in the higher circles of his university. Within a year he had again fallen foul of the wise men of Pisa.

One of the most prominent men in the district wished to dredge the mud from Leghorn harbor. Galileo saw a model of the proposed dredger and immediately said that it would be impossible to dredge the harbor with it. He was laughed at by the engineers and other men who claimed a much better knowledge of the subject than he. They carried on with the manufacture of the full-scale dredger, but in use it failed completely.

So angered were the would-be dredgers by Galileo's impudence in thus condemning their work — even although he had been proved correct — that they began to stir up extremely bitter feeling against him. He found his lectures at the university hissed at; he was deprived of a ducal patronage; and life was generally made so uncomfortable for him that despite his arrogance and powers of sarcasm he finally found it prudent to leave the university at Pisa and go to Florence.

Poor Galileo found that troubles seldom came singly. About this time his father died and he had to support the rest of his family. However, adversity was nothing new to him. He had been fighting it since his birth in 1564.

Although both his parents were of good family they were extremely poor. His father was a talented musician and mathematician who had learned by experience that these studies offered little financial reward. Galileo, his eldest son, displayed a marked skill at mathematics while still quite young, but his father was determined to have him educated as a doctor. By careful saving and sacrifice, his parents were finally able to send their son to the university at Pisa, and congratulated themselves on having sidetracked his love for mathematics.

Alas for their hopes; despite his new studies, his interest in mathematics and all things mechanical was always well to the front. He was still only in his teens when he discovered the law of the pendulum.

Kneeling at his devotions one day in the cathedral at Pisa, the young Galileo noticed that the great lamp suspended from the cathedral roof was swinging in a current of air. His interest quickened as he noticed that although the lamp was increasing the arc of its swing, it appeared to be traversing the greater distance in the same time that had been necessary for its earlier and shorter movements.

He looked around for some means of checking this observation more scientifically. But here in the cathedral — where he should have been at his devotions — he had no instrument to prove the accuracy of his findings.

And then his medical training came to his assistance. He used his own pulse rate to satisfy himself that the lamp was indeed covering wider arcs in the same time taken for small distances.

At the time, the only use that Galileo made of his discovery was to use it to measure the regularity of the pulse beat. But the knowledge was his, and after many years he applied the law of the pendulum to the construction of clocks. In our present world of rush and push, much depends upon the careful measurement of time. Today, we may take for granted the theory Galileo evolved from the lantern he saw swinging in the cathedral, but in those days it was as great a discovery as the electric computer of today.

If he had made no further contribution to the world of science he would have been remembered. But not only could he see the value of his own discoveries, he was also clever enough to adopt and improve the discoveries of others. His work of improving the telescope is a remarkable illustration of this faculty.

About this time there was in existence a telescope for use on land, which had been produced by a Dutch optician named John Lippershey. At first the discovery had been hailed only as a toy, "which has the power to bring far things near to the observer." It was left to Galileo to realize the full importance to which such an instrument could be put.

He had very quickly mastered the knowledge of lenses necessary to produce his own telescope, but whereas the Dutch production only had a magnifying power of three, Galileo contrived to make himself a telescope of a thirty-two power. And not for him was the passing wonder of seeing how near it would bring objects on land. He was far more concerned with the wonders of the heavens.

Directing his telescope to the sky, both by day and by night, his keen powers of observation had, within a year, supplied him with deductions which were amazing for his day and age.

Naturally enough, both the sun and the moon attracted much of his attention. Against all popular belief of his time, he asserted that the moon was not perfectly smooth and round with its own source of illumination, but was much like earth in that it had mountains and valleys with its sole source of light being that reflected from the sun.

For the first time, sunspots became visible and their movement was used logically to support Galileo's theory that the sun rotated from east to west and did not remain suspended in the heavens without movement of its own — as so many of his contemporaries believed.

Until then, the milky way had always been considered as some form of heavenly mist. Now, with the aid of his telescope, Galileo saw for himself the numerous stars which contributed to this phenomenon. He also found the moons of Jupiter and the phases of Mercury and Venus.

One can imagine him — now in his forties — sitting alone in his primitive observatory gazing ever upward at the heavens and marveling as his patience uncovered each new-found wonder. He saw enough to make him completely forsake the Aristotelian theory that the planets and sun moved around the earth. He now knew that the earth was not the center of the universe, but that with other planets it moved around the sun.

He was never the man to make a secret of his discoveries and, as more and more of his observations of the heavens became known, he found himself summoned to Rome by the Church to defend a charge of heresy.

When he found himself, in the year 1611, standing

before the Inquisition, he put forward his facts and argued as eloquently as possible. Not all the high church dignitaries were completely bigoted in their acceptance of ancient philosophies. They listened to him and then allowed his return to Florence, on the understanding that he would obey Pope Paul's injunction no longer "to hold, teach or defend" the newer doctrines.

This step by Galileo is hard to understand, for it was certainly out of keeping with his normal behavior. Previously he had always fought authority for the sake of science and now it appeared as if he had capitulated. But perhaps there was method in his meek acceptance of these terms. He was no longer bothered as he continued with his studies and writing. Completely happy in his own world of books and experiments, he could now work without hindrance, and this was the case for the next seven years. Then, strangely enough, he published a paper attempting to explain away comets as being tricks of reflected sunlight. This, one of his few major mistakes, was readily accepted by both his learned contemporaries and various dignitaries of the Church.

Emboldened by the success of this his first paper to

be published since his pact with the Pope, Galileo then wrote in dialogue form a book in which his belief in the new system of the world was made quite clear.

Immediately he was summoned to Rome again and was told that his teachings were a direct contradiction of those of the Bible. The men who tried Galileo followed the Bible teachings to the letter. Under threat of torture they made him agree to recant his belief that the earth revolved around the sun.

Galileo was now in his seventieth year, and saw that no real value lay in a prolonged quarrel with the Church. He was sentenced to life imprisonment and was condemned to recite once a week for three years the seven penitential psalms. Actually his sentence was much lighter than many expected or wanted. In all he spent only a few weeks in prison, and his stay there was comparatively comfortable.

Despite the sympathy of the church officials, however, the period of his trial and imprisonment aged Galileo considerably. Finally, Pope Urban ordered his release, and he returned to Florence. Here he still continued to work at his discoveries and write books on scientific data.

Then, in the evening of his life, came the greatest

blow. At the age of seventy-three he became deaf and blind. Even this failed to deter him and he continued to write with the help of friends, and to use his feeble limbs to further his discoveries. At this period his chief regret was that he could no longer see the glories of the heavens that he had revealed to others.

Five more years of the dark and silent life continued until at the age of seventy-eight the man who had fought adversity, jealousy and ignorance all his life died while dictating his ideas on the result of a moving body striking an immovable one.

His work was not doomed to the obscurity that his enemies would have desired. Galileo was the father of modern science. His refusal to accept theory unless supported by the proof offered by experiment set the pattern of men who were to follow him throughout the centuries. When the Italian Royal Commissions finally published his collected works at public expense, the data of his various experiments and discoveries filled twenty-one volumes.

He advanced the knowledge of his day over a wide range of scientific subjects that embraced light, motion, gravity and the laws of the solar system. Others improved upon his methods and inventions, but few scientists of any age could claim, "I am the first" quite as many times as this rebel who was born in Pisa some four centuries ago.

## EXPERIMENTS

### GALILEAN TELESCOPE

ONE of the most important of Galileo's discoveries was the telescope — and one of the least known is his air thermometer. We can make both of these instruments, and will begin with the telescope.

YOU WILL NEED: A biconvex lens, diameter 1½ to 2 inches (focal length about 12 inches); a biconcave lens, diameter 1½ to 2 inches (focal length about 1 to 2 inches); a large sheet of thin, strong cardboard; glue; black ink; brown paper; Scotch tape.

The tube of your telescope consists of two parts. Make the first part by rolling thin cardboard, about 11 inches long, around a broom handle. Glue the edge of the cardboard down and further reinforce the tube by passing several bands of Scotch tape around it. The inside of the tube should be painted black.

Roll a second piece of cardboard into a tube, about 6 inches long, so that it just slides inside the first. Glue the edge and reinforce with Scotch tape, as with the first tube. Ensure that while the small tube will slide easily within the larger a light-free joint is obtained.

The problem of securing the correct lenses is not as difficult

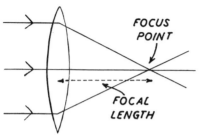

BICONVEX LENS CAUSES RAYS OF LIGHT PASSING THROUGH IT TO CONVERGE

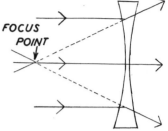

BICONCAVE LENS CAUSES RAYS OF LIGHT TO DIVERGE

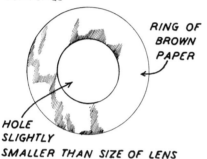

HOLE SLIGHTLY SMALLER THAN SIZE OF LENS

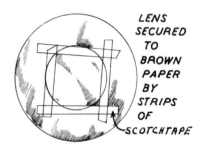

BROWN PAPER GLUED TO SIDES OF TUBE

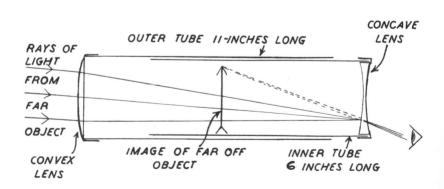

as some may fear. They can be obtained at some opticians' shops or suitable ones may be salvaged from old spectacles.

The convex lens must be secured to one end of the large tube and the concave lens to one end of the small tube. It is doubtful whether you will be fortunate enough to obtain lenses of exactly the required size to fit snugly into the home-made tubes. If they are larger than the tubes they may be Scotch-taped into position. If they are smaller they can be secured to the center of a ring of brown paper with Scotch tape; the edges of the brown paper then being folded down and glued to the tube, as shown in the accompanying diagrams.

Now fit the smaller tube to the larger so that there is a lens at each end. Look through the concave lens and focus the telescope on distant objects by sliding the inner tube back and forth.

### AIR THERMOMETER

YOU WILL NEED: A small bottle with a well-fitting cork; ink; water; glass tubing; white card; pencil.

The air thermometer works on the principle that when substances (in this case, air) become warm, they expand. The warmer they get, the greater is the amount of their expansion.

Begin by half filling your small bottle with water to which you have added a few drops of ink as coloring. Make a small hole through the cork and insert a piece of glass tubing about 12 to 15 inches in length.

Smear a little Vaseline around the cork before pushing it home into the neck of the bottle. The Vaseline will help to ensure an airtight fit. More Vaseline smeared around the glass

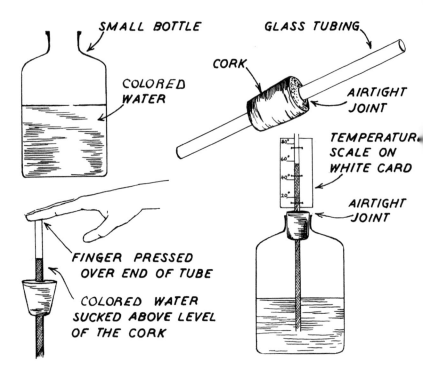

SMALL BOTTLE

GLASS TUBING

CORK

COLORED WATER

AIRTIGHT JOINT

TEMPERATURE SCALE ON WHITE CARD

AIRTIGHT JOINT

80°
60°
40°
20°

FINGER PRESSED OVER END OF TUBE

COLORED WATER SUCKED ABOVE LEVEL OF THE CORK

tubing where it is inserted in the cork will make an airtight joint here, as well.

Before putting the cork in the bottle, suck some of the colored water into the tube so that it reaches well above the cork. Retain it in this position by placing a finger tightly over the top end of the tubing as you remove it from your mouth.

Keeping your finger in position, push the cork and glass tube into the bottle so that the end of the tubing is well below the surface of the colored water. A piece of white card can be secured to the tube above the cork by two or three stitches of thread or fine wire.

Your thermometer will need a scale and the card can be used for this purpose. Place the bottle into a bowl of water whose temperature is already known (that is, boiling water, freezing water, etc.) and wait for the colored water to rise or fall to its new level and then carefully mark this position in on your scale. You may use either Centigrade or Fahrenheit markings. When completed, the air thermometer can be used as either a bath or room thermometer.

# CHAPTER IV

## OTTO VON GUERICKE (1602–1686)

ALL the morning people had been moving out of the German city of Ratisbon to the level plains a few miles away. They traveled by foot, by horse and by wagon — all with high hopes of being entertained. That idiot of Magdeburg, they understood, had said that he could make a ball of two pieces of bronze that would be so strong that two teams of horses would be unable to pull it apart. And what is more, he had invited the Emperor Ferdinand III and his royal court to watch the experiment.

It was a sunny day and they welcomed this break

from their work. Beer flowed freely and they were in a really good mood and quite ready for a laugh at Otto von Guericke's expense. Some of them even hoped the emperor would punish him for daring to bring him out on such a fool's errand. Although by now von Guericke was middle-aged, there were many who still regarded him as a rich young fop.

A great cheer went up as the emperor arrived with his followers. When the royal court had settled themselves, Otto von Guericke was seen carrying his two halves of a ball. The scientist's appearance was greeted with shouts of derision, but he was not in the least disturbed by the noise and laughter. Placing the hemispheres carefully on the ground, he doffed his hat and bowed deeply from the waist to His Majesty the Emperor. He repeated this performance to the crowd.

A born actor and very much of a showman, he was thoroughly enjoying himself. Striking a theatrical pose, he held the two halves of his globe up for all to see. Then he took a clean handkerchief from his pocket and started to polish the hemispheres. After an exaggerated scrutiny of each he placed them carefully together.

An assistant now brought an air pump over to him and this was fitted to the metal ball. There were shouts from the crowd because they thought he was seeking to trick them in some way. Otto promptly called upon two or three of them to inspect both the ball and the pump. They pulled the ball apart again and not until they were satisfied that there were no adhesives being used nor any secret device for locking the two halves together, did they permit him to begin work again.

The pump was fitted to the sphere for the second time and within a few seconds the metal ball had been emptied of air. Von Guericke freed the pump from the ball and called impatiently for the horses. Two laborers from a nearby farm came forward, each leading a team of four massive beasts.

The crowd hushed as Otto bowed to the emperor again and hooked each half of the ball to a team of horses. The attendants then led both teams apart so that the sphere was suspended in mid-air between them. Suddenly, at von Guericke's signal, each attendant flicked the flanks of his lead horse and the two teams lunged forward.

The crowd gasped as the horses strained in this novel tug-of-war without being able to separate the halves of the metal ball. It seemed miraculous. Here were eight horses pulling as hard as they could and the sphere still remained whole. Yet they had seen one of these horses pull a cartload of grain.

Highly delighted with the success of his experiment, von Guericke called for more horses to help. Still the two hemispheres remained together and the jeers of the crowd turned to cheers.

Not until two dozen horses were exerting their united strength against the vacuum he had created inside the metal sphere were the two halves finally wrenched apart. The emperor walked across to inspect this remarkable ball for himself and then turned to congratulate the scientist. Otto von Guericke still had another little trick he wished to show them. Once again air was pumped from the bronze sphere so that the two halves became clamped together. This time he turned a small tap at one end of the ball and permitted air to return and then showed them how simple it was for a man to separate the two halves.

It was in this remarkable fashion in 1654 that Otto von Guericke, the clown prince of science in the seventeenth century, displayed the knowledge that he had acquired about air pressure. He had in fact made the first pneumatic machine.

Unlike many famous physicists, von Guericke was born with all the advantages of wealth and rank. His birth took place at Magdeburg in Germany on October

20, 1602, and being without financial worries in his youth he was rather undecided as to what profession he should adopt.

After some consideration he turned to law, and he studied this subject at various universities in Germany, finally learning mathematics in Holland and also visiting France and England. Actually, his study of mathematics and mechanics displeased his family, but he found a growing interest in these two new subjects, and continued with them despite his parents' displeasure.

He first made his name during the Thirty Years' War, when he spent much time helping to fortify German towns. When Magdeburg itself was sacked by Tilly on May 10, 1631, he narrowly escaped with his life, but later returned to his home town to become its burgomaster. He then played a major part in rebuilding the town and planning new fortifications.

But although von Guericke was a brave man and a patriot, his main interest was science. Obviously he believed many of the incorrect notions of his time, but on several points he was not easily satisfied. In particular, the question of air pressure intrigued him and he was not as easily satisfied with current explanations as were most of his contemporaries.

Did air exert a constant, unchanging pressure? What would happen if all the air was sucked from a sealed object? These were two of the main questions which occupied his mind, and unlike most of the scientists of his day he did not blindly accept old laws and theories, but proceeded to perform practical experiments to satisfy his curiosity.

He soon saw that some form of pump was going to be a necessity, and he set to work to construct something that would prove suitable. Some of his earliest experiments with suction were doomed to failure. Once, in order to create a vacuum, he filled a wooden wine cask with water and tightly closed it. He then tried to remove the water by means of a brass pump — and succeeded only in breaking the connections between the cask and the pump.

With considerable resource, he found a means of strengthening the connection and tried again. This time it took three men pulling at the piston to draw some of the water out. But again the experiment failed. Air forced its way through the cracks of the wooden cask and so destroyed his attempt to create a vacuum.

He may have been a fop and an exhibitionist in many ways, yet he did not lack determination. He made

OTTO VON GUERICKE (1602-1686)

inquiries around the town until he found a copper-smith who agreed to make a large copper sphere. This had an outlet valve to it for connecting to a strong pump. He filled the sphere with water and then started to pump the water out. It proved to be hard work, but gradually the water was withdrawn. And then came disappointment again. The vessel had not been made perfectly spherical and had been beaten out too fine in its shaping, with the result that the sphere collapsed.

Von Guericke tried once again and, because he had carefully noted the reasons for his past failures, was able finally to produce a strong, perfectly spherical vessel, which this time stood up to the tests he imposed upon it. To his delight he was successful in obtaining a fairly good vacuum, and armed with the knowledge thus obtained he was enabled to stage his sensational demonstration with a metal sphere and two teams of horses.

Among other results of von Guericke's experiments was his invention of the air pump. It was a crude instrument compared with later ones, but it enabled him to carry out several experiments at varied pressures.

For one experiment he withdrew the air from a large glass bell-shaped container in which he had suspended a bell by a piece of thread. The bell was made to strike every few minutes by a carefully prepared clockwork mechanism. Starting up this mechanism, he then proceeded to pump the air from the glass container, and was intrigued to find that the sound of the bell became fainter and fainter as the air inside the jar diminished, until when all the air had been extracted no sound could be heard at all although the clapper could still be seen to strike the side of the bell.

Another time he lit a candle in the vessel and again withdrew all the air. As the air decreased, the flame became weaker until it flickered out. On one occasion, he placed a bird in the vessel and gradually pumped the air out. Within a short time the unfortunate creature had its beak wide open and was gasping for air, until finally, as the pump continued with its work, the bird gave a last convulsive struggle and died.

From his experiments there began to emerge many important facts, and among them was the knowledge that food could be preserved in a vacuum. Today this kind of preservation of food is taken for granted. We have vacuum-sealed cans and jars; we have vacuum flasks for keeping our drinks piping hot or ice-cold; and various other means of preserving our food and beverages.

# OTTO VON GUERICKE (1602-1686)

In von Guericke's day there was nothing like that. Brine was the universal preserver for fish and meats, while fruit and vegetables had to be eaten while fresh or allowed to go bad. For one of his experiments, von Guericke placed a bunch of grapes into his now famous glass bell and kept them perfectly fresh in a vacuum for six months. It is doubtful, however, whether at the time he fully realized the benefits his experiment would have for mankind.

From these early tests of the property of a vacuum he went on to something more mathematical. He weighed his vessel on the most accurate balance of the day and then weighed it when all the air had been extracted. It was less at the second weighing, which substantiated von Guericke's belief that air has weight. From this early experiment he arrived at a rough estimate of the density of air.

Progressing even further, he observed fluctuations in weight from day to day and he correctly attributed this to small variations in the pressure of the atmosphere. His findings enabled him to improve the air thermometer previously produced by Robert Boyle. Again his showmanship came to the fore and undoubtedly helped to make his thermoscope, as he called it, much more well-known.

His thermometer consisted of a copper sphere containing air. To this sphere was connected a U tube containing alcohol, which sealed the vessel. On the alcohol was a float from which a thread passed over a pulley and — here came his showmanship — supported the figure of an angel which indicated the temperature. When the air in the sphere expanded, the alcohol in the U rose, and the angel fell. Conversely, when the air contracted, the angel rose. He used a scale of six "degrees" which varied between "great heat" and "great cold." The rise and fall of von Guericke's angel became one of the showpieces of his time.

Down to the middle of the seventeenth century, the rise of water in the shaft of a pump was generally accepted as due to nature's dislike of a vacuum. In 1632, however, Galileo and other scientists of the day noticed that water would never rise above 32 feet. This led to an experiment by Torricelli, one of Galileo's pupils. He wanted to see how far mercury would rise in a tube. He suspected that it would rise about 27 inches and when, on his suggestion, Viviani made the experiment, his surmise proved correct. By 1659, Robert Boyle proved that the height of any fluid in a barometer depended upon the atmospheric pressure and also upon the density of the fluid in question.

## OTTO VON GUERICKE (1602-1686)

Then came an experiment by Otto von Guericke. He found it possible to raise water by suction from the ground floor of his house to the third story. Never could he draw it any higher. This puzzled him and in order to find out just how high water would go he made what he called his water barometer.

This consisted of four brass tubes joined end to end to form one long tube, with one end fitted to a glass receiver and the other to a tap immersed in a bowl of water. The tap was closed and the tube and the receiver were filled with water. When he opened the tap the water sank to a certain level which could clearly be seen through the side of the glass container and — again the touch of showmanship — which was indicated on a graduated scale by the outstretched arm of a wooden manikin floating on the surface. The difference in the levels in the tube and in the vessel could be determined by the use of a plumb line.

Von Guericke was convinced that the rise of the water depended on the pressure of the atmosphere and that it varied from day to day because of variations in the pressure. He made a detailed study of these fluctuations and tried to tie them up with the changes in the weather. One day the sudden drop in the level of the water worried him because it was far greater than any he had noticed before. He began to wonder whether the fluctuations of the water level were not, after all, just results of bad measuring and poor construction.

Further reflection convinced him that he had every reason for faith in his calculations. With typical vanity, and courage, he decided to make public what his barometer foretold. It was 1660 and weather forecasting was still a thing of the distant future, but he predicted a terrific storm. His faith in his barometer proved justified, for the storm came exactly as forecast by him, and he achieved wide acclaim as the man who could foretell the weather to come.

At once scientists throughout Europe began to investigate the connection between barometric height and the weather. Crude mechanical devices for this purpose were brought into being by Boyle, Meriotte, Halley and other learned men of the time.

By now some of the people of his town were beginning to regard von Guericke as something of a magician who was in league with the devil. How could any ordinary man foretell the weather or restrain two teams of powerful horses with a sphere? His next experiments did little to allay their fears.

Electricity, as we know it, was not even in its infancy

## OTTO VON GUERICKE (1602-1686)

when von Guericke invented the first electric lamp.
Inspired by the work of Boyle, von Guericke — who
was now aged forty-five — cast a ball of sulphur in a
glass bowl. Then he broke the glass away from the orb
of sulphur and fixed this latter to a spindle and spun
it round and round. When friction was applied to the
revolving ball of sulphur, sufficient electricity was gen-
erated to cause it to glow. The first electric lamp had
been born.

With his electric machine, von Guericke also discovered that there are two kinds of electricity — later
to become known as positive and negative. He found
that if a substance is attracted by an electrified body
and touches it, it is at once repelled. This we know now
is because an electrified body tries to share its power
with a nonelectrified one. Having done so, they no
longer agree, because like repels like.

What must have really hurt von Guericke's showman's pride was the fact that his work in the electrical
field did not attract anything like the attention that
his earlier experiments had done. Simple though his
experiments may seem to us today, they were the result
of much diligence and ingenuity. Like many other
great physicists, he was born too soon. When he dis-

73

covered electric light there was no thought of being able to put it to practical use. It was 200 years later before electric lighting became common knowledge.

## EXPERIMENTS

### AIR PRESSURE

WHILE Otto von Guericke's experiments with electricity failed to attract the attention which he may have desired, the following experiments with air pressure will show the startling power latent in our atmosphere and will, perhaps, explain why von Guericke's own work in this direction achieved so much notoriety.

We cannot use teams of horses to perform his Magdeburg Sphere demonstration, but we can still repeat this in a different form to reveal the existence of air pressure.

YOU WILL NEED: A 1-pound jam jar; a preserving lid, clip and rubber ring*; a drill; a bolt; cold solder; washers; saucepan; string; plywood.

Through the center of the preserving lid drill a hole just large enough to take a ¼-inch-diameter bolt. Clamp the bolt firmly to the lid with a nut and washer on either side. Cover the nuts and washers with cold solder (sold in small tubes) so that the joint is quite airtight.

Pour a little cold water into the jam jar and stand the jar in a saucepan of water which is brought up to boiling point. Wait until the water inside the jar is actually boiling and then snap

---

* A canning jar which has a lid with a rubber washer and a screw ring can be substituted.

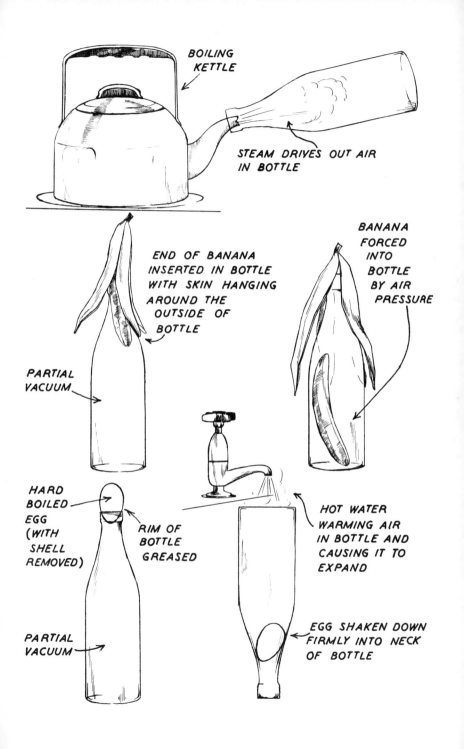

BOILING KETTLE

STEAM DRIVES OUT AIR IN BOTTLE

END OF BANANA INSERTED IN BOTTLE WITH SKIN HANGING AROUND THE OUTSIDE OF BOTTLE

BANANA FORCED INTO BOTTLE BY AIR PRESSURE

PARTIAL VACUUM

HARD BOILED EGG (WITH SHELL REMOVED)

RIM OF BOTTLE GREASED

HOT WATER WARMING AIR IN BOTTLE AND CAUSING IT TO EXPAND

PARTIAL VACUUM

EGG SHAKEN DOWN FIRMLY INTO NECK OF BOTTLE

the lid on the jar over the rubber ring. Remove the jam jar from the saucepan (taking care not to scald yourself) and set it aside to cool.

At this point we have achieved the following; when the water in the jar boils, the steam thus created pushes most of the air out of the jar. The mouth of the jar is covered by the lid at the height of this action, and the jar is allowed to cool. When the steam cools it becomes water again — occupying only a small fraction of the space that it filled as steam. The preserving lid, with its spring fitting and rubber washer, ensures an airtight seal, and as no air can re-enter the jar to replace the steam, a partial vacuum is created.

When the jam jar is cool, remove the spring clip, and support the jar in an inverted position (but not over the best carpet — even great physicists had their mishaps!), as shown in the diagram.

Drill small holes in each corner of a small piece of plywood and suspend it from the bolt with lengths of string. Now place a weight (say about 10 pounds) on the plywood. If your experiment has been successful this weight will be easily supported. The reason is that the outer air, in trying to enter the vacuum in the jar, is exerting pressure on the lid. By adding more weights to the plywood some idea of the great pressure of air can be gathered.

In fact, it is possible to perform this experiment with reasonable accuracy. First obtain a good vacuum in the jar, and then add weights until the lid finally falls away. Divide this final weight by the area of the lid in square inches. Air pressure is about 15 pounds per square inch. How accurate was your own experiment?

# OTTO VON GUERICKE (1602-1686)

IT is an easy matter to see why early physicists were often thought to be magicians in league with the devil. Even such a common force as air pressure can be used to produce quite startling results. The following experiments will no doubt mystify some of your friends.

YOU WILL NEED: A milk bottle; kettle; banana; hard-boiled egg.

Hold the bottle (with a teacloth or towel) so that the spout of a boiling kettle fills it with steam. Pull the skin free from the end of a banana and immediately the bottle is filled with steam insert the end of the banana into it, allowing the flaps of skin to hang over the edge.

Hold the banana firmly on to the mouth of the bottle so that it acts as an airtight "cork." As the bottle cools, the steam inside will condense and the outer air will attempt to force its way into the area of low pressure in the bottle.

As the mouth of the average milk bottle is approximately 1 square inch in area, there will be something like a 15-pound pressure being exerted on the banana — sufficient to force it slowly down into the bottle and peel it at the same time.

A similar experiment can be performed with a hard-boiled egg. First remove the shell from the egg without damaging the surface of the egg white. Prepare the bottle again by holding it over a boiling kettle until it has filled with steam. Now insert the narrower end of the egg into the mouth of the bottle and press it down gently until it has formed an airtight joint (a smear of butter may help). Once again, as the outer air attempts to enter the cooling bottle, the egg will be forced down through the narrow neck.

77

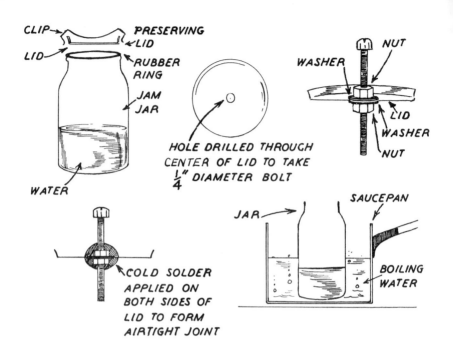

CLIP — PRESERVING LID
LID
RUBBER RING
JAM JAR
WATER

HOLE DRILLED THROUGH CENTER OF LID TO TAKE $\frac{1}{4}$" DIAMETER BOLT

NUT
WASHER
LID
WASHER
NUT

COLD SOLDER APPLIED ON BOTH SIDES OF LID TO FORM AIRTIGHT JOINT

JAR
SAUCEPAN
BOILING WATER

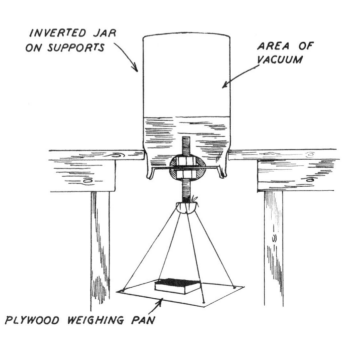

INVERTED JAR ON SUPPORTS
AREA OF VACUUM
PLYWOOD WEIGHING PAN

## OTTO VON GUERICKE (1602-1686)

To many, the problem may be not so much how the egg got into the bottle, as how best it may be retrieved. To perform the experiment in reverse, as it were, hold the bottle under the hot-water tap so that the air in the bottle becomes warmed and tries to expand. If the egg has been shaken down firmly into the neck of the bottle it will serve rather like an inner cork. The increasing pressure of the expanding air, however, will act upon the egg and force it back through the mouth of the bottle.

# CHAPTER V

## SIR ISAAC NEWTON (1642–1727)

ALMOST as though it was obedient to the scientific needs of the moment, the year 1642, which saw the death of that great pioneer, Galileo, also witnessed the birth of Isaac Newton — a genius of physics.

He was born at Woolsthorpe, a tiny hamlet about seven miles from Grantham in Lincolnshire, in rather tragic circumstances. His father died before Isaac was born and left little for his heir to inherit. He proved to be a very sickly baby and it was said that he was so small that he could easily have been put into a quart pot.

He proved a remarkable illustration of "brain before

brawn," for although he remained weak and timid, with a distaste for games as he grew into childhood, he also soon showed a natural flair for mechanics.

His mother remarried by the time her son was three and left him to be brought up by his grandmother. Until the age of twelve he attended the village school at home, but was then sent to a grammar school at Grantham. Being several miles from home, he went into lodgings with a Mr. and Mrs. Clark who were friends of the family.

In Mr. Clark he found a true friend who encouraged him to use tools and make the models which occupied so much of the boy's leisure time. Also living with the Clarks at this time was a little girl called Storey, and Isaac delighted in making her doll's furniture and similar toys.

One of his best models was that of a new windmill that had been built on the road between Gonerby and Grantham. It gave him great delight to watch the millwrights at their work. Before they had finished their mill, his own small model was working happily on the roof of the house. If the wind failed, he had arranged a simple little mechanism so that a pet mouse, whom he called Miller, could set the model working.

He also made a carriage that could be worked by hand — probably a forerunner of the self-propelled wheelchair; a clock that depended for its motive power upon regular drips of water; the first "sun clock," which was then called Isaac's dial and which we now know as a sundial; and numerous kites and similar apparatus to help him measure the strength of the wind.

Indeed, at one time, Isaac had many of the neighbors thoroughly frightened by his antics with kites. He fixed paper lanterns to their tails and flew them at night. We wonder how many men were sent scampering home from the inn, swearing never to touch a drop again, as they saw strange lights ducking and weaving through the night sky!

Despite his cleverness with tools, he did not at first shine at his subjects at school. The truth was, his mind became so occupied with his toys and models at home that at school he became downright idle. Then something happened which may have helped change the scientific history of the world. He was kicked in the stomach by a bigger boy. Although he was small and timid, his temper had its breaking point. He came from yeoman stock, and with determination he fought back until he had thoroughly thrashed the bully.

This set him thinking. If he could beat this boy — who was well above him in class — physically, then he could certainly beat him mentally. From that moment he worked so hard at his subjects that he was soon at the top of his class, and eventually became head of the school.

But, by the time that Isaac was sixteen, his stepfather died and his mother needed him to help run her farm. For this occupation, however, he showed absolutely no talent. On his weekly trips into Grantham with their produce he would leave all the buying and selling to an old servant and disappear into Mr. Clark's chemist shop for a few hours to read books on chemistry. At home he continued to make models and to study, and it was soon clear to his mother that he would never make a farmer.

Soon Isaac Newton was back at school. At eighteen he left Grantham for Trinity College, Cambridge. When he arrived in June, 1661, it was just after the Restoration of Charles II and many of the leading scholars had left. He was allowed to enter the college as servant to his tutor, which meant that he was allowed free tuition in return for his work.

His first years at Trinity, where he studied Greek,

Latin and mathematics, were nothing out of the ordinary. Soon he found, however, that he was well in front of the lectures that he must attend. Then came another fateful move for Isaac and the world. The eminent Isaac Barrow transferred from the professorship of Greek to a new chair of mathematics, founded by Lucas in 1663. It was not long before he noticed Newton's great ability. He encouraged the young man in his studies, and at the age of twenty-two, Newton took his B.A. degree.

A temporary halt followed. In 1665 the outbreak of the Great Plague closed the university and Newton returned to Woolsthorpe for two years. At home, he says, he looked back on the years at Trinity with great pride and was anxious to return. But it was at Woolsthorpe that he made some of his greatest discoveries.

He worked out the method of differential and integral calculus at a time when Barrow, Pascal, Wallis and other great mathematicians were still only on the brink of the discovery.

He solved the area of the hyperbola for the first time and carried out his answer to fifty-two places of decimals. He also discovered the binomial theorem and the general method of expression of algebraical functions in infinite series, which was almost as great a feat as the calculus itself.

He loved the study of optics, and ground lenses for hour after hour. In attempting to make a telescope through which objects could be seen without having their edges distorted with a fringe of color, he realized that white light could be resolved into these separate color rays. Having little success with his telescope when using lenses, he struck out in a different direction — the reflecting telescope which magnifies by reflection from a mirror.

The idea was not Newton's, but James Gregory's. But where Gregory had failed to make a reflecting telescope, Newton succeeded. It was about six inches long with a metal mirror about one inch in diameter, and the whole mounted on a sphere so that it could be pointed in any direction.

Newton presented a copy of this instrument to the Royal Society. It was the first of his great achievements to be acknowledged, and for this he was elected a Fellow of the Royal Society in 1672. Unfortunately he could not make his own astronomical observations with any accuracy because he was shortsighted.

Then came the incident which has become so famous — Newton and the falling apple. The story is that he was seated or lying under the shade of an apple tree, thinking over the problem of how the stars and planets could keep going. The apple tumbled to the ground (some reports have it that the apple landed on poor Newton's head) and it suggested to him that the force which controlled motion on earth also applied to the bodies of the universe.

Immediately he attempted to seek an answer to the problem: if the apple falls to the earth, why does not the moon fall? He studied all he could find of the works of Galileo and other physicists, attempting to prove that the greater the distance between two bodies the less the attraction. But at the time there was no accurate figure for the size of the earth, and deciding it would be impossible to prove his theory, he put the whole problem to one side.

In the year 1672, however, a scientist named Picard published a far more exact set of figures dealing with the earth's dimensions. Stirred by this new information, Newton went back to those calculations on gravity which he had shelved for seven years. By brilliant, patient study he finally worked out the complete theory of gravitation but, typically, he refrained from publishing the information.

By now, he had returned to Cambridge, and quietly

continued with his studies in mathematics, optics and dynamics. Still a young man, barely out of his twenties, he had yet achieved a lifetime's work — most of which he had done little to publicize.

It was in 1669 that Newton had a stroke of fortune. In that year, Isaac Barrow resigned his professorship in Newton's favor. This new position gave him an income of about £200 a year — which in those days was probably worth ten times as much as today, or about $5,500 — and the work entailed only twenty-four lectures and fifty conferences a year.

His first course of lectures as a professor dealt with optics. They proved so brilliant that news of them reached the Royal Society. His reflecting telescope, mentioned earlier, was inspected by Charles II, Christopher Wren, Hooke and several other leading scientists and mathematicians.

Two years later, he made another deep impression on the Royal Society with a paper on his discovery of the spectrum and the resolution of white light into colored rays. At this time it seems he had acquired a liking for tennis and, in his explanation of how the rays of light are bent by a prism, he remarks that he "had often seen a tennis ball, struck with a racket, describe such a curved line."

This first paper of Newton's remained the pattern of research method ever since. Experiment and theory are combined with a ruthless cutting of all frills. Every point mentioned has a bearing on the case; not a word is wasted.

Even quiet, retiring Isaac Newton was not without his enemies, however. Contemporary with him and his work on light was another great scientist, Robert Hooke, who was acknowledged as the professional experimenter to the Royal Society. In 1665 Hooke had published his own book on optical work called *Micrographica*, and he now alleged that Newton had borrowed many ideas from that book.

To everyone's surprise, Newton made no defense against these charges. In fact, he asked the Royal Society if he could resign his fellowship, but this they would not accept. Later, it was realized that, although Newton had not used any of Hooke's ideas, he was too sensitive to bring argument before the public's gaze. Another reason was his wish to pursue his studies without any further distraction.

Hooke was elected Secretary of the Royal Society in 1679 and at once wrote to Newton asking if he had any further scientific news. Newton answered with his theory about the earth's rotation and gravitational force, to which Hooke replied that Newton had erred. Later, Hooke tried to claim as his own some of Newton's findings, although he could produce no proof to support his claim, obviously lacking his rival's keen mathematical brain.

At this time, Edmund Halley, a young astronomer, was seeking information about the movements of planets. Neither Hooke, Wren, nor any of the other great men of the Royal Society could help him, and he finally visited Newton at Cambridge.

To the young astronomer's amazement, Newton not only solved his problem for him, but proved many other points that had been concerning physicists of the time. Halley at once saw the importance of Newton's work and implored him to write them out clearly and offer them to the Royal Society for publication.

This led to a wonderful scientific book, *Principia Naturalis,* which Newton completed in fifteen months. In it he deduced the general movement of bodies on earth and in the heavens, as well as supplying solutions to hundreds of other physical problems.

The Royal Society was greatly impressed with the *Principia,* but neither Newton nor the Royal Society could afford the cost of publication. In the end, his friend Edmund Halley paid for publication of the book that brought world fame to Newton.

It was while his book was awaiting publication that Isaac Newton appeared in one of the most dramatic episodes of his life. With others, he defied James II, and finally had to stand up against the notorious Judge Jeffreys for the rights of his university. The next year James II fled, however, and Newton found himself involved in politics.

Gradually, the strain of work began to tell upon him. He complained of insomnia and failing appetite and became irritable and absent-minded. One morning he left a candle burning in his room and in the resulting fire several important papers were destroyed. He became increasingly moody and downcast.

However, by 1694 he was almost his old self again and a year later there came a surprising offer. William III decided to make Newton his Warden of the Mint. When he learned that the position carried an extremely good salary and would also permit him to carry on with his studies, he accepted it.

One of his first jobs involved the catching of counterfeiters. He turned his great intellect as readily to this as to any of the scientific tasks he had undertaken. He

compiled casebooks, he interviewed criminals and supplied his agents with disguises. Eventually he caught
the prince of forgers of that day — Challoner, a wealthy
man who was backed by a number of influential poli-
ticians.

His mathematical knowledge and careful study of
accounts turned him into a first-class administrator,
and his skill in science enabled him to start a system of
recoinage. He was appointed Master of the Mint with
a substantial increase in salary. Toward the end of his
days he was earning something like £2,000 a year and
had saved £32,000, a veritable fortune in those days.

In 1703 he resigned his chair at Cambridge and was
elected President of the Royal Society. Two years later
he was knighted by Queen Anne.

The years went by. Newton, gray from the age of
thirty, still retained his modesty and shyness despite his
growing fame. He would never spare himself in study,
but would think nothing of working eighteen hours
straight on a problem. Then, on the 28th of February,
1727, he went against his doctor's wishes and attended
a meeting of the Royal Society. Arriving home very
tired he went to bed, and never really recovered. On

the 18th of March he lost consciousness and passed away in a state of coma two days later.

For a week his body lay in state before being buried in Westminster Abbey. And so passed one of the greatest men in mathematics and physics the world has ever known. The modesty and humility that characterized him can be best expressed by one of his own sayings:

I know not what the world may think of my labors, but to myself it seems that I have been but as a child playing on the seashore; now finding some prettier pebble or more beautiful shell than my companions, while the unbounded ocean of truth lay undiscovered before me.

## EXPERIMENTS

### NEWTON'S COLOR DISC

IT may be remembered that it was while Newton was making and using telescopes that he became interested in color. He discovered that if all the colors of the rainbow are mixed, the color produced is white, and that white is not really a color at all but a mixture of all these colors: red, orange, yellow, green, blue, indigo and violet. This is how we can prove it.

YOU WILL NEED: Cardboard; compass; pencil; scissors; bradawl; string; paints and brush.

Draw a circle 8 inches in diameter on a piece of stout white cardboard. Cut this disc out and with a bradawl pierce two

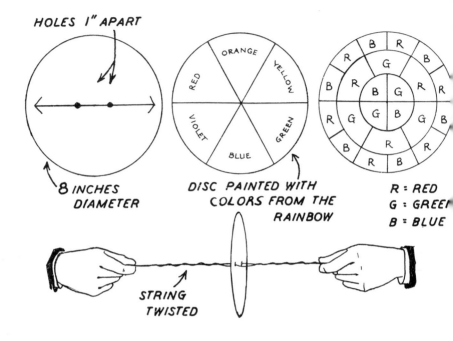

HOLES 1" APART

8 INCHES
DIAMETER

DISC PAINTED WITH
COLORS FROM THE
RAINBOW

R : RED
G : GREEN
B : BLUE

STRING
TWISTED

holes opposite each other, about ½ inch each side of the center, as shown in the diagram.

Divide the cardboard disc into six equal portions, and paint each portion one color of the rainbow (indigo may be omitted). The reverse side of the disc can be divided into three or four concentric rings. Different pairs of colors may then be painted in consecutive order around this side of the disc.

A 4-foot length of string should now be threaded through the two holes in the middle of the disc, and its two ends tied together. Hook a forefinger in each end of the string, revolve the disc until the string is tightly twisted, and now by pulling and relaxing upon the ends of the string the disc can be made to revolve at great speed.

It will be found that when the disc is revolving fast, the colors appear to mix together and form white. On the reverse side, depending upon which colors have been chosen, many effects may be observed.

### SPLITTING WHITE LIGHT

NEWTON found that the sun gave out light containing all colors of the rainbow, combined to form what we see as ordinary white light. We can perform exactly the same experiment as Newton used to prove this.

YOU WILL NEED: A sunny room; brown paper; a mirror; a biconvex lens; a prism; white cardboard.

If possible, choose for this experiment a small sunny room with only one window. Cover the window with thicknesses of brown paper until it is completely blacked out. Make a pinhole through the brown paper so that a narrow sunbeam enters the room.

Now arrange a mirror so that it catches and reflects the beam of light. Direct this reflection so that the beam is passed through a convex lens which focuses the rays of light. If a prism is placed in the path of these focused rays, they will be bent, but as red light bends less than orange light, and so on, when they pass through a prism a band of colors (known as the spectrum) will be produced and may be caught on a screen of white cardboard.

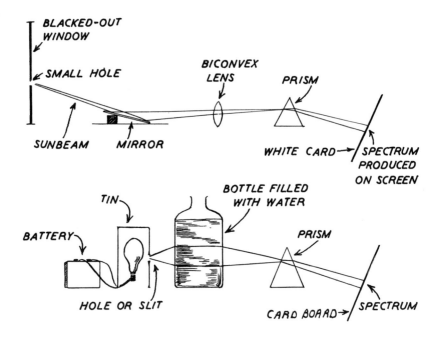

As an alternative experiment, use a beam of light from a 6-volt or 12-volt car headlight run from a battery. The bulb should be covered with a can from which a narrow slit has been cut. A beaker or cylindrical bottle filled with water could be used instead of the convex lens for focusing the rays on the prism. Quite probably you will find that although a spectrum is produced by this means, because an artificial source of light has been used, it will be inferior to the one obtained by focusing sunlight through a prism.

# CHAPTER VI

# BENJAMIN FRANKLIN (1706–1790)

BENJAMIN FRANKLIN was born in Boston, Massachu-
setts, on January 17, 1706. He was the tenth son of a
family of seventeen and the frugality he learned in his
youth remained with him, even when wealth and fame
were his.

Franklin's father was a tallow chandler and soap-
maker. At one time he had hopes of dedicating his
tenth son to the ministry but found it necessary, after
Benjamin had received only a few years' schooling, to
set the lad to work with him.

Benjamin Franklin had no great love for the work
in his father's business. He detested the smell of molten

tallow and found the task of cutting wicks, filling candle molds and cleaning out the vats anything but to his taste. The few coppers he earned from his father he spent on books, and these, together with a keen interest in witty and stimulating conversation, were his only means of education until he reached the age of twelve.

Whether he fell out with his father at this time or whether he tired of soapmaking, we do not know, but he left his father to take up an apprenticeship as a printer with his half brother, James.

This new trade proved far more suited to his talents and soon he was recognized as one of the best craftsmen in the office of the *New England Courant,* and while still in his early teens he was attracting attention by his articles in that publication. Finally, when James Franklin found himself in jail for some of his own rather outspoken writings, it was Benjamin, at the age of seventeen, who took complete charge of producing the newspaper until his brother was released.

James returned to the office within a few weeks, but Benjamin, now freed from his indentures, left his brother to seek his fortune elsewhere. We next hear of him landing at Market Street Wharf in Philadelphia, then little more than a village of timber dwellings.

Hungry, and exhausted after his journey, he followed several of the inhabitants to a Quaker meeting-house. Entering with them, he seated himself and immediately fell asleep and remained asleep throughout the service. A humble introduction for one who was to see Philadelphia grow in size and prominence, and where, just over half a century later, Benjamin Franklin was to be one of those who drafted the terms which were to create the United States of America.

His knowledge of the printing industry and his facility with the written word had soon found him employment. He worked long hours to save money and to increase his skill in his chosen trade. By the age of twenty he was made manager of a newspaper and printing business, and he was soon obsessed with ideas for producing his own newspaper.

Realizing that the American newspaper profession was a long way behind that of England, he went to that country to buy type and to study English methods. His knowledge of printing soon gained him employment in London and he remained in England for some eighteen months. During this time he was noted for his abstemious ways, but despite his thrifty habits there was nothing of the kill-joy about Benjamin.

# BENJAMIN FRANKLIN (1706-1790)

He was an accomplished swimmer, and he surprised his companions once, when they were traveling by boat from Chelsea to Blackfriars, by slipping over the side into the water and swimming the remainder of the distance. So much skill did he display in the water that he was almost persuaded to remain in England and open a school for swimming.

He clung fast to his first ambition, however, and returned to Philadelphia, where, after a brief partnership, he started in business for himself in 1730. Among his many other distinctions, he was one of the pioneers of the American press. His earliest publication, under the title of the *Pennsylvania Gazette,* was later renamed and now enjoys a great deal of publicity combined with a large circulation under the name of the *Saturday Evening Post.*

So successful in his business transactions was he, and so charming in his manner, that when he was thirty he was appointed Clerk to the Pennsylvania Assembly. By the time he had reached middle age he had a reputation for being one of the most public-spirited and ablest men in the state.

But, for all his public life, Benjamin Franklin was still the experimenter, and there is little doubt that had he felt free to follow his own devices once his personal fortune was assured, he would have made science his chief study — and his main interest electricity and electrostatics.

Electricity was nothing new in Franklin's day, but it was he who turned attention to what he called the electrics in the atmosphere. Thunderstorms had for years been regarded as the explosions of gases in the upper atmosphere, and lightning as the wrath of gods. People were still content to believe what ancient philosophers had put forward.

Franklin was skeptical, however. For years he had recorded several important similarities between lightning and the electrical discharge from a Leyden jar, although he made the mistake of assuming that electricity itself was a weightless, invisible fluid. He entered all his findings in a notebook and on November 7, 1794, he wrote:

Electrical fluid agrees with lightning in these particulars: giving light; color of the light; crooked direction; swift motion; being conducted by metals; crack or noise in exploding; subsisting in water or ice; rending bodies as it passes through; destroying animals; melting metals; firing inflammable substances; sulphurous smell.

# BENJAMIN FRANKLIN (1706-1790)

It was after he had published these observations that he started on his famous kite experiments. He proved that the electric sparks produced by static electricity were a force similar to lightning flashes, although it is doubtful if Franklin fully realized the immense power that he was attempting to tap when he sent his home-made silk kite soaring aloft during a thunderstorm, or the personal danger in which he stood.

The kite, made from a large silk handkerchief, was furnished with a steel point and tied to a hemp string. The end of the string was secured to a length of silk, a key being fastened where the hemp and the silk joined. After a time, both Franklin and his son, who accompanied him in the experiment, noticed that the loose fibers of the string were standing up. When they touched the key they received a distinct shock. In fact, the key conducted so much electricity that Franklin was able to charge a Leyden jar with it.

The American newspaper owner counted himself fortunate in thus being able to prove the theories which he had published. How fortunate he had actually been was made clear shortly afterward, when a Swedish scientist electrocuted himself while trying to verify Franklin's work by attempting the same experiment.

The name of this Boston printer, author, statesman and scientist was by now a household word in England, and in 1753 he was awarded the Copley medal by the Royal Society. Reasons for the award were cited as "on account of his curious experiments and observations on electricity . . . deserving well of the philosophical world and their learned body in particular."

Two years later, the Royal Society elected him a Fellow and waived his fees. He often attended their meetings and served on the Council of the Society for four years.

His dangerous experiments with lightning did not end with his kites, however. He caused an iron bar to be erected some nine feet above his chimney and continuing down inside his house to the hallway opposite his room door. The bar terminated in a pair of wires, each bearing a small bell at the end. Between them, suspended on a length of silk thread, was a brass ball, and as storm clouds above his house charged the iron bar with electricity, the ball was attracted to the bells and rang them. By the aid of this ingenious but dangerous device, Franklin was informed when it was suitable for him to conduct further experiments.

As you may well imagine, one result of his work was

the invention of the lightning conductor. But in the beginning these were viewed with much suspicion. Questions were raised in Parliament as to whether or not the lightning "rods," as they were called, would attract lightning and so increase rather than lessen the danger. Some even argued as to whether knobbed rods were to be preferred to pointed ones.

In 1769 the authorities in charge of St. Paul's Cathedral asked the Royal Society for the best method of protecting their building, for another church had been struck by lightning and badly damaged. They were recommended that "there should be a complete metallic communication between the cross of St. Paul's and the dome with the water pipes used as conductors."

Three years later the government, concerned because some Italian powder magazines had been destroyed by lightning, asked the Society the same question. A committee of five was appointed. Four of them advocated pointed rods, but the fifth protested and claimed that a knobbed conductor would be safer because it would neither increase nor invite the electricity.

This created quite a storm among the learned heads of England. Franklin refused to be drawn into any such argument. Writing on the subject to a friend, he said: "Here are some electricians that recommend knobs instead of points on the upper ends of the rods from a supposition that points invite the stroke. It is true that points draw electricity at greater distances in the gradual silent way but knobs will draw at the greatest distance a stroke."

The government added up the pros and cons and finally decided upon points. But while this controversy raged, Franklin was in Paris and the War of Independence was taking place. Because Franklin was an American, those who supported the pointed rod theory became identified with the Americans — and were none too popular. People paid more attention to the national than the scientific factor.

Even King George had the lightning conductors on his palace changed from points to knobs and he asked the president of the Royal Society to change its ideas and resolutions supporting the points. The president, Sir John Pringle, replied: "Sire, I cannot reverse the laws and operations of nature."

Franklin still refused to take any part in the argument. He claimed to have fully proved his findings in a paper to the Society, and he had no wish to defend his scientific opinions further. If they were right, he said, truth and experience would support them. If wrong, they would be rejected.

Weld, a writer of that time, summed up the whole matter when he wrote:

> While you great George for knowledge hunt,
> And sharp conductors change for blunt,
> The nation's out of joint;
> Franklin a wiser course pursues,
> And all your thunder useless views,
> By keeping to the point.

Although Franklin the scientist is chiefly remembered for his kite experiment, he had other work to his credit. He was instrumental in applying the terms "negative" and "positive" to electric charges. He also produced an electric-charge storer and it became known as Franklin's plate.

This consisted of an ordinary pane of glass with a large sheet of tinfoil pasted to each side. By connecting this to a frictional machine it became possible to store an appreciable amount of static electricity. Today we know that such an instrument would serve no useful purpose, but the fact remains that Franklin had taken one of the earliest steps in the storage of electricity.

In order to prove that certain colors absorb heat while others reflect them, Franklin once spread a number of differently colored pieces of cloth over snow upon which the sun was shining. Upon examining the snow underneath each piece of cloth, a few hours later, he discovered that the snow beneath the white cloth had been scarcely affected by the sun's rays, that the snow beneath the black cloth had melted quite considerably, and the snow beneath other colors had melted at varying but lesser degree than that beneath the black cloth. He therefore argued that white clothes would afford the maximum relief in hot weather by reflecting the sun's rays.

Even quite trivial phenomena attracted and held his attention until he had solved them to his satisfaction. Once, during a sea voyage, he noticed how calm the wake of the vessel became after several tubs of greasy refuse had been emptied over the stern. Upon his arrival in England, he experimented with oil on ponds and lakes and then published his findings on the manner in which oil could control the surface of troubled water.

As early as 1736, when he lost one of his sons by smallpox, Franklin stated that he wished he had given him the disease by inoculation. Dr. Edward Jenner, who discovered the secret of vaccination, did not make his first experiment until 1796.

Great scientist though he was, Benjamin Franklin was also a remarkably good statesman. Because the Americans recognized his worth he was sent to England as their ambassador just before war broke out between Great Britain and its colonies. Franklin realized that war was imminent and did all he could to prevent it. He returned to America to find that the War of Independence had already begun.

He became a leading figure in the American government which helped to give America her freedom from British control. While war was still going on he was sent to Paris as American ambassador to gain the support of France against the British. He returned once again to America, and was mainly responsible for opening the negotiations which led to peace between Britain and America.

He was constantly fighting against slavery in the United States. Although it was many years after his death that slavery was abolished, it was his pressure that really got the people thinking about the horrors of the slave system.

After remaining in Paris as U. S. minister until 1785, he returned to Philadelphia to be elected president of the state's executive council. He was subsequently re-elected for the two following years and then retired from public life. He died in Philadelphia — now a prosperous city and no longer the village of his teens — on April 17, 1790, at the age of eighty-four.

His tomb is in Christ Church cemetery at the junction of Fifth and Arch streets, Philadelphia — close to where he had carried out his kite experiment. Those who bemoan the fact that they never had a chance in life should remember Benjamin Franklin. One of a poor family of seventeen children, by dint of hard work and perseverance he rose to become one of America's greatest figures, a man who gave freely of his services, first for his community, then for his country, and finally for the world.

## EXPERIMENTS

### POSITIVE AND NEGATIVE ELECTRICITY

BENJAMIN FRANKLIN'S main contribution to science was connected with the study of static electricity. He also introduced the terms "positive" and "negative" as applied to electrical force. He was mistaken, however, in believing that bodies contained electrical "fluid."

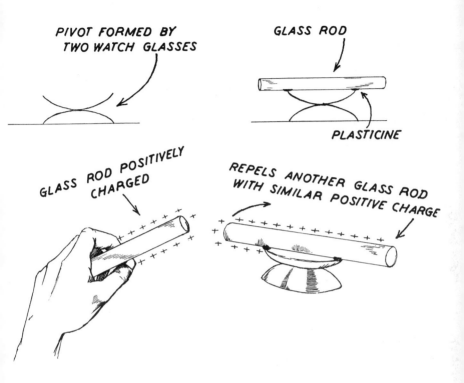

PIVOT FORMED BY TWO WATCH GLASSES

GLASS ROD

PLASTICINE

GLASS ROD POSITIVELY CHARGED

REPELS ANOTHER GLASS ROD WITH SIMILAR POSITIVE CHARGE

His theory was that all bodies contained this fluid to varying degrees. If the body contained the correct amount it showed no signs of electrical charge, but if the fluid was decreased it showed negative electrification, and if increased, positive electrification.

For example, if we rub a glass rod with silk, Franklin would maintain that some of the fluid from the silk was absorbed by the glass rod and as the latter would now have more than its normal share of fluid it would show a positive charge, while the silk, with less fluid remaining, would show a negative charge.

We now know that there is no electrical fluid in bodies, but if we say "electrons" instead of fluid, Franklin's idea of electrification holds fairly good even today, except that loss of electrons leads to a positive charge and vice versa.

On no account will we repeat Franklin's very dangerous experiment of flying a kite in a thunderstorm, but we can investigate further substances which become negatively or positively charged and produce a "flash of lightning."

YOU WILL NEED: Two watch glasses; plasticine; two glass rods; piece of flannel.

Two watch glasses are needed for this experiment. If you are unable to obtain these at home, they can often be bought for a few cents at secondhand dealers or a watch repairer's, etc. One glass is placed face upward on a flat surface with the second glass balanced face downward on the first. A thick glass rod is balanced on the top watch glass so that it lies horizontally — retain it in this position with plasticine (see diagram).

This first glass rod, which must be dry and clean, should be rubbed vigorously with a flannel cloth. This will give the rod a positive charge. A second glass rod, similarly charged by rubbing with flannel, held in the hand — or better still in a dry rubber glove — is brought near the rod balanced on the watch-glass pivot. Providing this is done in a warm dry room so that both rods retain their electrical charge, the pivoted rod will turn away from the second rod.

# BENJAMIN FRANKLIN (1706-1790)

Repeat the experiment, but using a length of rubber tubing in place of the second glass rod. The rubber tubing will be negatively charged and on approaching the pivoted rod there will be evidence of attraction.

Both glass rods, being similarly charged with electricity, repel each other; the unlike charges of the glass and rubber, however, attract each other.

Different materials can be tried on the pivot or held in the hand, such as glass rods, rubber tubing, polythene rods, lengths of plastic hose pipe, ebonite rods, plastic pens and mechanical pencils, etc. They can also be rubbed with a variety of material: silk, flannel, fur, etc.

Find out which materials become negatively charged and which become positively charged. After much experiment it will be found that some substances become charged when rubbed and others do not. Those which become charged are called "insulators" and those that show no charge are called "conductors."

## AN ELECTROPHORUS

THIS machine was really first invented by Volta in 1775. It obtains an electrostatic charge by means of induction, and it is possible to make this charge flow through the air like lightning.

YOU WILL NEED: Candles; saucepan; sulphur; sealing wax; two tin lids; gas ring.

To make an electrophorus we need two flat tin lids, one slightly smaller than the other. Melt one or two candles in a can placed in boiling water and remove the wicks. Stir pow-

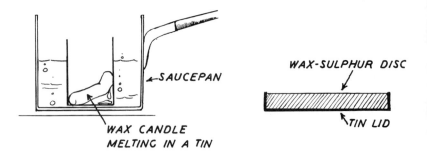

SAUCEPAN

WAX CANDLE
MELTING IN A TIN

WAX-SULPHUR DISC

TIN LID

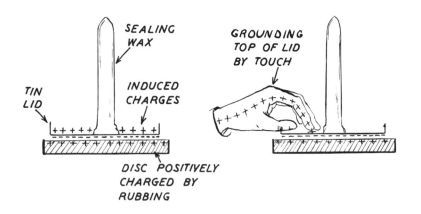

SEALING
WAX

TIN
LID

INDUCED
CHARGES

DISC POSITIVELY
CHARGED BY
RUBBING

GROUNDING
TOP OF LID
BY TOUCH

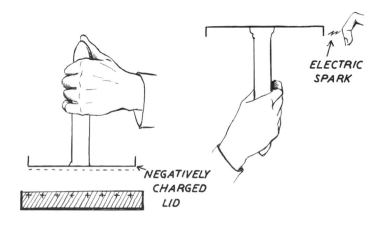

NEGATIVELY
CHARGED
LID

ELECTRIC
SPARK

dered sulphur into the wax until the mixture becomes very thick (sulphur can be obtained from pet shops or druggists). Pour the mixture into the larger tin lid until it is completely full. Allow it to set.

Heat one end of a large stick of sealing wax and press it into the inside center of the smaller lid so that they become fixed together.

Now rub the sulphur-wax disc briskly with a flannel cloth and so cause it to become charged with static electricity. Place the small tin lid flat on the disc. The positive charge on the disc of wax induces a negative charge on the underside of the lid and a positive charge on the upper surface of the lid.

The charge on the upper surface is removed by allowing it to ground by touching it with your finger. Now remove the lid, taking care to hold it by its sealing-wax handle. The lid will still contain the negative electric charge. If it is brought near a conductor such as a piece of grounded metal or even the knuckle of one's finger, a spark will be given off which can be seen, heard as a crackle and, if the knuckle is used, felt as a slight prickle.

The sound corresponds to thunder and the flash of the spark to lightning, although both, of course, are very much smaller than that produced by nature.

# CHAPTER VII

# LUIGI GALVANI (1737–1798)

SIGNORA LUCIA was ill. She had not been feeling well for several weeks and now she was refusing to eat.

"I do not feel hungry," she told her anxious husband, when he pleaded with her to eat so that she might maintain her strength.

"Can't I tempt you with anything?" Luigi Galvani asked his wife.

"There was a dish that I liked many years ago," his wife replied. "A broth of frogs' legs."

She had a devoted husband. All that morning he searched the market place of his native Bologna until he finally found a stall selling edible frogs. He took some home in his hat — still alive.

Galvani hangs frog's legs
onto iron railings and
watches them contract.

This was to be the first of many similar errands. The doctors told Galvani that his wife was attacked by a disease of the chest and they warned him that she must be given as nourishing food as possible. Since the one food which seemed to please Lucia was frogs' legs, he used to personally prepare them for her.

One morning, having killed a frog and skinned its large, fleshy legs, he placed them on his laboratory table, close to an electrical machine, while he went to fill a bowl with water. He had rested one of his fine, anatomical knives on the legs he had just skinned.

When his wife entered the room and looked on the table she was startled to see the severed legs of the frogs moving in a strange, spasmodic manner. She hastened to tell her husband, and since Lucia Galvani also had some knowledge of electricity, she gave it as her opinion that a current from the electric machine was flowing through the dissecting knife and causing the frog's legs to move in such a surprising manner.

Her husband lost no time in proving her theory. While the electric machine was working he placed the point of the knife on first one leg and then the other. Each time, the frog's legs moved. When he repeated the experiment with the machine switched off, however, he received no answering movement from the legs.

"These legs will need hanging," he told Lucia. "And then I'll prepare the broth."

He hooked the legs over the iron kitchen rail with some copper hooks. He then received his second surprise of that day. As the legs swung against the iron rail they jumped and twitched violently, although they were not, this time, in contact with any discharge from his electricity machine.

At this stage, Galvani knew that he had discovered something of importance about electricity but did not know quite what it was.

"There must be an electric charge produced by some fluid in the nervous system of the leg," he told Lucia. "This is a remarkable discovery."

His wife smiled at his eagerness and reminded him that he had been about to make her some broth rather than conduct electrical experiments. Rather shame-facedly he unhooked the frog's legs and carried on with the cooking. But the problem possessed him for several days. Finally, he decided that the movements of the legs on the second occasion, when no electric current had been present, had been caused by some form of animal magnetism about which nothing was known. He felt sure that the convulsions had been brought on by electricity that was naturally present in the frog's leg itself.

History does not record whether Lucia enjoyed that particular meal but it is certain that Galvani paid further visits to the stall in the market place to obtain more frogs.

He wondered whether a discharge of lightning would produce the same effect on the frogs' legs that he had already observed. It was a stormy day, with a strong hint of thunder in the air, that day in 1790 as he removed the legs from another frog, ran a copper skewer through them and suspended them from an iron railing.

Sure enough, as soon as the legs were suspended from the railings they began to jump and convulse in a most energetic fashion. Much to his surprise, he also discovered that this extraordinary effect could be obtained on fine days when there was no hint of lightning or thunder, and also at any time of the day that he chose to make the experiment.

Armed with the results of numerous experiments with the frogs' legs, Galvani hastened to record his new theory on "animal magnetism." He arrived at the conclusion that all animals possessed an electric power that was inherent in their organism. That this power was secreted by the brain and distributed to all parts of the body by nerves. He considered the muscles as a form of condensor, charged on the outside by a positive electric charge and on the inside with a negative one. Thus, he claimed, did the muscles form natural Leyden jars.

Galvani failed to realize, as did his contemporary, Volta, that the electricity had been formed by the action of two dissimilar metals: the copper skewer and the iron railings, in contact with moist animal tissue.

Strangely enough, it was Galvani's incorrect theories which were accepted by the electricians of his day. Others carried out similar experiments to verify facts for themselves, but accepted Galvani's answer as to why the frogs' legs reacted as they did.

It was not until Volta, in 1800, discovered the "voltaic cell" that Galvani's theories were disproved.

Luigi Galvani — sometimes called Aloisio Galvani — was born in Bologna in 1737 and was brought up in a strictly religious atmosphere. His early days were spent studying theology, for it was his intention to enter a monastery. But his friends and, strangely enough, his father opposed this idea and succeeded in persuading him to study medicine.

He took up this new study with the same energy that he had previously shown for his theological studies. By early manhood he had already won for himself the reputation of being one of the finest surgeons of his time, and when, in 1762, he wrote a brilliant treatise on the formation of bones, he was awarded the professorship of anatomy at Bologna University.

Here, his reputation grew. He proved himself a good teacher and his lectures were always well attended. His brilliant surgical work and his continued researches into anatomy assured him of fame.

Unfortunately, Signora Lucia Galvani never really recovered from her illness, and she died in 1790. Deeply distressed by the loss of his beloved wife, Galvani did little work after this.

"My heart," he would tell his friends, "is like an electric machine without electricity. It just will not go."

During the political troubles in Italy, when his country was invaded by Napoleon, Galvani refused to ally himself to the new Cisalpine Republic and was deprived of all his honors. So great was his fame by this time that the government restored these to him without demanding an oath from him.

He died on December 5, 1798, still arguing bitterly with Professor Volta of Pavia University about the merits of each other's theories in the electrical field.

Galvani died believing that he was right and Volta was just a fool. Had he lived two years longer, however, Galvani would have died a most unhappy man, for it was in 1800 that Volta proved that it was Galvani who had erred in his judgment.

## EXPERIMENT

ALTHOUGH Galvani gave an incorrect explanation for his discovery of the production of electricity by using two different metal plates, his name is remembered and honored by the naming of electrical instruments and processes after him — galvanometer, galvanized metal, etc.

A galvanometer is an instrument for detecting small electric currents and the direction in which they flow. We can make a type of galvanometer very simply.

### GALVANOMETER

YOU WILL NEED: A cardboard tube about 3 to 5 inches in diameter; several feet of thin, cotton-covered copper wire; two 2-inch nails; a piece of wood measuring 6 inches x 6 inches x ½ inch;

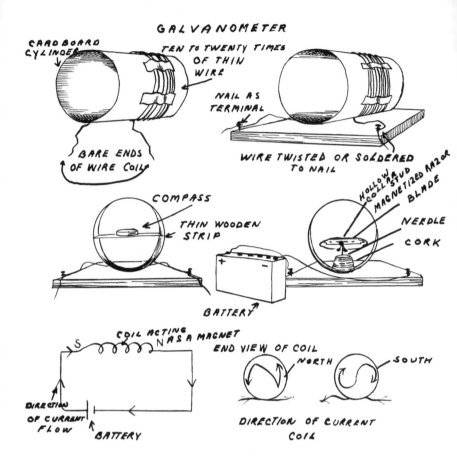

GALVANOMETER

CARDBOARD CYLINDER

TEN TO TWENTY TIMES OF THIN WIRE

NAIL AS TERMINAL

BARE ENDS OF WIRE COIL

WIRE TWISTED OR SOLDERED TO NAIL

COMPASS

THIN WOODEN STRIP

BATTERY

HOLLOW COLLAR STUD

MAGNETIZED RAZOR BLADE

NEEDLE

CORK

COIL ACTING AS A MAGNET

END VIEW OF COIL

NORTH

SOUTH

DIRECTION OF CURRENT FLOW

BATTERY

DIRECTION OF CURRENT COIL

a small charm compass or an old razor blade and magnet; a hollow collar stud, needle, cork, adhesive paper or glue.

*Method of Construction*

1. From the cardboard tube cut a cylinder measuring some 3 inches in diameter.
2. Wind the wire onto the cylinder leaving 6 inches of wire free at the beginning and the end. Between 10 to 20 turns

will be sufficient and these can be held in place on the cardboard cylinder by adhesive paper.

3. Now glue the cylinder to the center of a wooden base. A drawing pin may help to make this join more secure, but care must be taken to ensure that the wire coils are not damaged when the pin is passed through the cardboard into the wooden base.

4. The two nails act as terminals and should be hammered into the wood at opposite corners of one edge (see diagram). The free ends of the wire are then twisted tightly about the terminals. Even better contact would be made by soldering the wire to the nails.

5. A length of flat wood, as long as the diameter of the cylinder and as wide, is obtained and a small compass is glued to the center of the wood. The wood is now carefully placed inside the cylinder so that it forms a neat little platform across the center of the cylinder, with the compass uppermost. It is important that the compass should be actually within the wire coils.

## How the Galvanometer Works

When an electric current is passing through the wire, a magnetic field is set up around the wire. If the same wire is looped or wound into a coil this magnetic field causes the coil to act as a magnet, with one end of the coil acting as a north pole and the other end as a south pole.

When two north poles or two south poles are brought close together they repel one another.

If we place the galvanometer so that the compass needle is pointing north and south and connect the terminals to the positive and negative terminals of a battery, the compass needle will be deflected. When a current flows, the coil acts as a magnet and the north pole of the coil will repel the north pole of the compass's magnet. If we reverse the current the coil reverses its poles and the magnet will be deflected in the opposite direction.

The size of the current will be proportional to the amount that the needle is deflected. The direction that the current flows will be shown by the direction in which the needle is deflected.

If a compass small enough for the galvanometer cannot be found, magnetize a razor blade by stroking it with a magnet, glue it to a cardboard disc, and mount it through the center hole on a collar stud and a needle inserted in a cork base. Find which end of the blade is the north pole and mark it with pen or pencil. Glue the cork base inside the cardboard tube, as shown in the accompanying diagram.

# CHAPTER VIII

# ALESSANDRO VOLTA (1745–1827)

In electricity, probably more than in any other field of science, the names of discoverers and inventors have been perpetuated in the findings that they gave to the world.

There is Galvani with galvanism; Ohm with his law; Ampère and his discoveries; and the famous Italian physicist whose name has now become a household word — Volta.

Alessandro Volta. The scientist who hardly ever left Como, his home town.

Alessandro Volta. The scientist who knew he was right, even though the world acclaimed Galvani in one of the bitterest controversies ever known in the world of science.

Volta was born in Como in 1745 — eight years after the birth of his rival, Galvani. He had descended from an old and noble family of Milan, which had lost both its power and wealth in the years following the Renaissance.

Like many other Southern Europeans, Volta reached a maturity of intellect at a much earlier age than other scientists of northern latitudes. Always a diligent student, he was noted for his brilliant versatility. Indeed, at one time, it was this very same versatility which caused him to hesitate between the rather divergent ambitions of becoming either a poet or a scientist.

Science finally won, although probably at the expense of literature. At the age of eighteen, Volta was devoting himself to the study of electricity. Within a few years he had both designed entirely new pieces of electrical apparatus and evolved a further theory on the Leyden jar.

It was this work, together with his diligently continued study in his special science, which earned him such a high reputation that by the age of twenty-nine he was offered an appointment as professor in physics at Pavia University.

Even before this appointment, however, Volta had written his first treatise. It was "On the Attractive Forces of Electric Fire," and he produced it while still only twenty-four years of age. He also designed further apparatus, chief among which were two instruments for generating electricity by induction.

In 1792 he wrote to the Royal Society of London telling them of his discoveries and theories. So impressed were the Society members by his work that he was awarded the Copley medal.

Other famous scientists now began to realize that growing up among them was another brilliant worker in the field of physics. In response to their invitations, Volta made one of the few journeys to take him away from his native Como. He traveled to France and England in order to make the personal acquaintance of other students of electricity and to exchange information with these fellow workers in his own particular sphere of science.

He returned to Italy and later found that Galvani, a professor of anatomy at Bologna, had offered him both inspiration and a challenge. Galvani, with his now famous experiment with frogs' legs, reported that he had discovered a form of animal magnetism.

# ALESSANDRO VOLTA (1745-1827)

Volta studied Galvani's findings and, although by now they had received international acceptance, immediately proclaimed them false. He demonstrated how the copper skewer and the iron railing used by Galvani in his experiment were the sources of the electric current which had led Galvani to believe that his frogs' legs had emitted their own form of magnetism.

For some time, Volta had suspected that the use of dissimilar metals such as iron and copper in moist surroundings was the vital factor in producing electricity. It was his work on Galvani's theory which convinced him that electricity could be produced by chemical means.

He instanced such action as the metal taste when holding a silver and gold coin against the tongue.

Then there came the day when Volta produced the first electric battery. This was to prove a notable milestone in the study of electricity.

During the early part of the nineteenth century, the only known way of producing a current of electricity was through the medium of friction. Electricity was produced in those early days by machines which applied friction to some nonconducting material.

Volta's battery, or "voltaic cell" as it became known,

proved to be the easiest method of producing a strong current of electricity that had so far been devised. However, simple as the method was, it took Volta at least eight years of careful experiment to perfect it to his satisfaction.

In the beginning, he placed a number of discs of tin and silver or copper alternately, and separated them with a cloth moistened with ordinary water.

Further experiment showed him that acidulated water could produce a stronger current of electricity. He filled a number of glasses with a very weak solution of acid and dipped into each glass, alternately, a strip of copper and a strip of zinc, the zinc being wired to the copper in pairs.

In this way, Volta produced what he called a "crown of cups" from which he obtained, for those days, quite a large amount of electric power.

Volta proved that the electricity he obtained by this chemical method was exactly the same as that produced by friction.

This discovery of Volta's was his greatest and practically his last. He was never a confident man and he personally felt that he did not have the talents necessary to advance further into the mysteries of electricity.

# ALESSANDRO VOLTA (1745-1827)

He appeared content to retain the professorship at Pavia and lead other students along the right road.

But in domesticating the fundamental natural force which we call electricity, Volta can be said to be the founder of many of our modern industries. His greatness was certainly recognized in his own lifetime, for in 1801 Bonaparte invited him to Paris in order to demonstrate his experiments and he was awarded the gold medal by the French Institute, of which he was elected a member. On the establishment of the French Empire in 1810, Volta was made a Count and Senator of the Kingdom of Italy.

Little is known of Volta's private life except that he married and had three sons. He died at Como on March 5, 1827, aware that the world was accepting his theories, although it is doubtful whether even he realized that his name would live on for so long and appear in most homes of the civilized world.

## EXPERIMENTS

As WE have seen, it was Volta, following experiments made by Galvani, who was able to explain how electric current could be produced by the chemical action of two plates of different metals immersed in a liquid conductor or electrolyte.

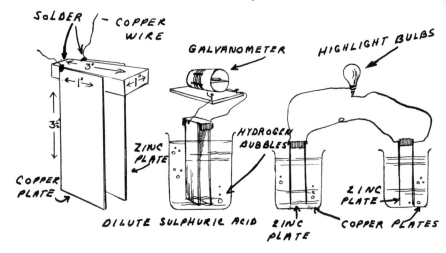

SOLDER COPPER WIRE
GALVANOMETER
HIGHLIGHT BULBS
3"
1"
1"
3½"
ZINC PLATE
HYDROGEN BUBBLES
ZINC PLATE
COPPER PLATE
DILUTE SULPHURIC ACID
ZINC PLATE
COPPER PLATES

A simplified explanation of the voltaic cell is that the metal plates react with the solution in which they are immersed. The chemical energy produced by this reaction is transformed into electrical energy which will be driven through a circuit if the two plates are connected. The voltage produced depends upon the type of materials used and not on the amount of materials.

It is possible for us to make a similar cell to that invented by Volta. This electric cell will consist of: a strip of zinc, a strip of copper, and dilute sulphuric acid. Should these items prove difficult to acquire, it will be possible to improvise to some extent.

Your strip of zinc can be obtained by cutting the casing from an old flashlight battery. This casing is made of zinc, but it should be well cleaned before use.

If strips of copper cannot be found, obtain a length of thick copper wire and hammer it flat. Sulphuric acid may be bought by name or as "oil of vitriol" from hardware stores or garages, but if you can find an old automobile battery the liquid it contains will be dilute sulphuric acid. Care must be taken when handling sulphuric acid because of its dangerous corrosive powers. Should any of the acid accidentally spill or splash onto skin, clothing or furniture, etc., it must be immediately washed away with repeated douches of cold water.

*Method of Construction*

1. Solder a length of copper wire to each strip of zinc and copper. The strips of metal should measure about 3½ inches by 1 inch.

2. Nail both strips, one to each side of a small block of wood measuring some 3 inches by 1 inch, as shown in the accompanying diagrams.

3. Pour dilute sulphuric acid into a jam jar or glass beaker until it is three-quarters full. Connect the wire from each metal plate to the terminals of the "current detector." Suspend the plates in the dilute acid in such a manner that they neither touch each other nor the sides or bottom of the vessel in which they are placed.

Watch closely and you will see how the zinc plate reacts with the acid so that bubbles of hydrogen are produced. These bubbles may be observed to move over to the copper plate, whereupon an electric current will pass through your small galvanometer and the needle of the compass will be deflected. Note the size of the deflection and the direction. After a short time the current will cease and the needle of the galvanometer will return to normal position.

This latter action of the compass needle is due to the collecting of hydrogen bubbles over the surface of the copper plate, thus preventing the electric charge from reaching the copper and traveling through the circuit. Remedy this by removing the plates from the acid, washing them under cold water and then drying them. When the plates are replaced, the current will flow once more.

The voltage produced by such a cell is almost 1.2 volts. If two cells are made and joined in series (i.e., the copper plate of one cell joined to the zinc plate of the other cell) sufficient voltage is produced to light a flashlight bulb. The simple circuit for this is shown in the diagrams. Remember that even with a double cell the current will not flow for long. If it is to be restored, the plates must be washed and dried.

Always remove and wash the plates before storing the cells. If they are stored with the plates in the acid the zinc plates will dissolve.

The simple cell of Volta's changes chemical energy to electrical energy, as we have seen. The lead storage battery uses electrical energy to cause a chemical change and then, by reversing this chemical reaction, we can obtain much of the electrical energy that we have put into the storage battery. In a way, our battery stores electrical energy in the form of chemical energy. We can extract this electrical energy by reversing the chemical reaction.

### LEAD STORAGE BATTERY

YOU WILL NEED: 2 plates of lead (an old piece of lead piping can be obtained and cut to size, 3½ inches x 1 inch x ⅛ inch); a jam jar or glass beaker three-quarters filled with

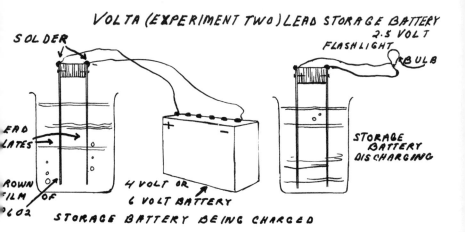

VOLTA (EXPERIMENT TWO) LEAD STORAGE BATTERY

SOLDER

2.5 VOLT
FLASHLIGHT
BULB

LEAD
PLATES

BROWN
FILM OF
PbO2

4 VOLT OR
6 VOLT BATTERY

STORAGE
BATTERY
DISCHARGING

STORAGE BATTERY BEING CHARGED

dilute sulphuric acid; some copper wire; a battery from 4 to 6 volts; and a flashlight bulb.

Set up the lead plates so that they may be suspended in the acid, as for the simple cell. Now connect the lead plates to the battery. The electric curent from the battery, flowing through the storage battery, causes a chemical action.

Bubbles will be seen around the plates, and the plate connected to the positive of the charging battery will become coated with a chocolate-colored layer of a chemical (lead peroxide). After charging for about 15 minutes, disconnect the storage battery from the battery and connect it to the flashlight bulb. The bulb will light up for about one minute. After this time the storage battery will have given up the electricity made by the chemical reaction and the bulb will be extinguished. At this stage, notice what has happened to the lead plates.

Your storage battery can be recharged as before and the bulb relit any number of times.

# CHAPTER IX

# MICHAEL FARADAY (1791–1867)

ANY biography of Michael Faraday must read like a success story, not necessarily to be subtitled, "From Rags to Riches," for throughout his career, Faraday gave of himself without thought of financial reward. Certainly, however, it is a story which tells of a rise from boyhood poverty to world fame.

In his early days, how many people could have guessed that the boy delivering newspapers in London would one day go down in history as the Father of Electricity — the man whose experiments have today made possible our telegraph and telephone, vacuum cleaners and washing machines; in fact the countless applica-

tions of electricity and electromagnetism upon which our civilized communities depend.

Michael Faraday was born on September 22, 1791, in a dismal cottage at Newington Butts, Surrey. His father was a blacksmith, and in defiance of the lusty tradition of that trade, suffered from ill-health. His frequent absences from work had an adverse effect upon his business, so that by the time Michael was five years old his parents had to move to shabby rooms above a stable in London.

We have little record of Michael Faraday's early life and education, although we learn something of the poverty which encompassed his family. Michael himself once stated that his mother would give him a large loaf on Monday of each week to last him the whole seven days. He would carefully mark the loaf into fourteen parts, so that he might have two for each day.

During his childhood he somehow managed to master the elements of reading, writing and arithmetic, but his education at this stage was confined to the same narrow limits that were imposed upon similar poor children of that time.

IIis stay at day school could not have been sufficient for him to have advanced far beyond the rudiments of education. By the age of thirteen he had entered regular employment as errand boy to a George Ribeau, a newsagent and bookbinder of Blandford Street.

At that time, newspapers were expensive and poor people hired them for a limited time. It was part of young Michael Faraday's duties to arrange for the distribution and collection of his master's papers. Another task was to dust and clean the lodging room over his master's small shop. During this time, the room was occupied by a French refugee artist who took an interest in the lad and gave him lessons in art and drawing, which later proved so useful to Faraday when called upon to illustrate his scientific work.

At the end of a year, his employer was so pleased with his errand boy that he offered him an apprenticeship as a bookbinder, without charging him any premium. Young Faraday thrived in this bookish atmosphere. His master used to buy up sheets of printed matter and bind them into volume form. Faraday's spare time was now spent in reading the pages which he had to bind during his working hours.

It was in this way that he first became interested in science; articles on electricity in an unbound copy of an encyclopedia, and a popular chemistry book of those days, *Marcet's Conversations on Chemistry,* being responsible in those formative years for turning his interest to the ever-deepening study of chemistry and electricity.

Life was still a struggle for the Faradays. His father died in 1810 and his mother had to support herself and family by taking in lodgers. When Michael started to attend evening lectures on natural philosophy, it was his elder brother, also a blacksmith, who helped him to pay the necessary shilling fee for each visit.

And so we find him, in his late teens, pursuing a detailed study of chemistry and electricity, with his leisure hours spent in undertaking many simple experiments to test the facts of his reading. With the family income so limited, his equipment was of the simplest and most inexpensive order, but his enthusiasm for experiment was already laying the foundation for a talent which was to bring him world acclaim.

Even so, it is doubtful whether he would have succeeded in effecting such an early entrance to the Royal Institution had he not had the stroke of good fortune to attract the attention of one of his master's customers, a certain Mr. Dance. Mr. Dance was a member of the Royal Institution himself, and noticing Faraday's studious habits and interest in matters scientific, he offered to take him to the last four lectures of a series which Sir Humphry Davy was giving.

We can imagine Michael Faraday's excitement, for Sir Humphry was the most famous scientist of the day. He duly attended the lectures, was fired with fervent admiration for the great man, and finally decided to give up his trade as bookbinder and to seek entry into the Royal Institution in whatever menial position became necessary.

Faraday gives us some insight into his mind at this time if we study his writings of the period. He states: "I took notes [during the four lectures] and afterwards wrote them out more fairly in a quarto volume. My desire to escape from Trade, which I thought selfish and vicious, and to enter the service of Science, which I imagined made its pursuers amiable and liberal, induced me at last to take the bold step of writing to Sir Humphry Davy, expressing my wishes and a hope that if an opportunity came his way, he would favor my views. At the same time I sent the notes I had taken of his lectures."

Sir Humphry himself was a self-made man who owed to his own genius and industry the fact that he had escaped from a dull, uninspired calling, so that when, one day in December, 1812, he received Faraday's letter and the bound volume of his lectures, the young man's plea for employment at the Royal Institution did not receive an unsympathetic hearing, as can be judged by the letter he wrote in reply to the young man:

Sir, I am far from displeased with the proof you have given me of your competence, which displays great zeal, power of memory, and attention. I am obliged to go out of town and shall not be settled here again until January; I will then see you at any time you wish. It would gratify me to be of any service to you; I wish it may be in my power.

I am, Sir, Your obedient, humble servant.

H. DAVY

Michael Faraday was overjoyed at the reception given his request. To his disappointment, however, when he finally met Sir Humphry, although the great man treated him with marked kindness, he pointed out that a laboratory career could hold but few prospects. In fact, he so far sought to dissuade Faraday from a scientific calling as to offer him all the bookbinding of the Royal Institution as well as to recommend him to his friends.

It must have been something of a bitter pill for

Davy's young disciple to swallow. But fortune favored him again — and with all the drama of a story book. Less than a month later, just as he was retiring for the night, there came a loud, imperative knocking at his door. With considerable surprise, he found a liveried footman outside, waiting to deliver a message from Sir Humphry. He was asked to call at the Royal Institution the next morning.

And on that following day, Michael Faraday was appointed as Sir Humphry's laboratory assistant, at a wage of 25 shillings a week, and two rooms for his occupation at the top of the Institution.

Once again, Faraday's industry and application to detail set him above his fellows. Just as Ribeau, his old newsagent employer, had rewarded his industry with a premium-free apprenticeship, so now do we find Sir Humphry Davy realizing that here was more than an ordinary laboratory assistant. Within a few months Faraday was being entrusted with more important work, where once again he could evoke his talent for experiment.

Still aware of his own lack of general education, Michael Faraday devoted a great deal of his leisure hours to self-improvement. But less than nine months after joining the Royal Institution, he was offered an experience likely to prove of inestimable value in his education: to accompany Davy on a tour of Europe.

Strangely enough, France and England were at war at the time. It says much for Sir Humphry Davy's reputation that Napoleon was instrumental in granting permission for the journey to be made. Actually, Europe was in a turmoil, for it was in the winter of 1812–13 that Napoleon had been forced in retreat from Moscow. Yet on October 13, 1813, Sir Humphry Davy, his wife, her maid, and Michael Faraday left London by coach for Plymouth.

Always a meticulous man, Faraday kept notes of his journey, which are still preserved. Although the only English they saw in France were prisoners of war, such was Sir Davy's reputation that his small party traveled in perfect safety, being accorded courteous hospitality by famous scholars and scientists of the day.

The tour lasted for two years, and in the beginning, Faraday records that his life was made miserable by Lady Davy's humiliating treatment of him. Unlike her husband, she regarded Faraday as a servant and took pains to exert her authority over him.

But despite this, the young man profited immensely

by the large amount of experimental work he had to undertake with Sir Humphry at the various seats of learning that they visited in France, Germany, Switzerland and Italy. At Florence he examined Galileo's first telescope — a simple tube of wood and paper, about 3½ feet long, with a lens at each end — and marveled at the accomplishments of a scientist born over two hundred years before himself.

He met many illustrious scientists during the tour — such men as Ampère and Volta, who spoke with him earnestly on electrical matters and stimulated his already great interest in the subject. It is fitting, perhaps, that as a result of Michael Faraday's own discoveries in electricity, the terms "ampère" and "volt" now serve as common reminders of his two great contemporaries in this field.

Upon his return home in 1815, Faraday was promptly re-engaged as Davy's assistant at the munificently increased wage of 30 shillings per week! By now, although he had only been with Sir Humphry for a little over two years, the great man was placing an ever-growing reliance upon his brilliant disciple.

And, indeed, they had come far together in so short a time, sharing dangers of laboratory experiments which abounded in unknown risks for the researcher and suffering many a minor injury in the chemical operations in which Davy was engaged. Six weeks after his return home, he assisted Davy in experimental work on the detonating compound of chlorine and nitrogen (now known as nitrogen trichloride) which is extremely explosive. He mentions this work in a letter: "I do it at my ease, for I have escaped — not quite un-hurt — from four different and strong explosions of this substance."

By now, his skill as a laboratory assistant was becom-ing increasingly known to those who lectured at the Royal Institution. His services in the setting up of ap-paratus for experiments to illustrate their lectures were in keen demand. Since Michael Faraday had to be present at these lectures to assist in their demonstra-tion, it follows that over the years he was gaining a re-markably thorough knowledge of all matters scientific.

With little more than his wage of 30 shillings, in 1821 he became married, at the age of twenty-nine, to Sarah Bernard. She proved an ideal wife for him, pro-viding the simple joys of home life which were all his modest character demanded — although daily he was meeting and conversing on equal terms with many of the noted scientists of his time.

## MICHAEL FARADAY (1791-1867)

With the Royal Institution now both his home and his laboratory, he began to experiment in new and untried depths of science. No longer was he regarded as Davy's assistant, but as a brilliant fellow worker, for together they had made a number of important discoveries in chemistry, particularly in the field of electrolysis — the breaking up of chemical compounds by passing an electric current through them while in solution.

In 1824 he gained the highest scientific honor that can be given in England, when he was made a Fellow of the Royal Society — an honor given for original research work affording valuable additions to scientific knowledge. And upon Sir Humphry Davy's retirement in 1827 he succeeded him at the Royal Institution.

His experiments now began to cover a vast field of scientific research, but some of the most important of these were connected with electricity. Up to that time, electricity was regarded as little more than a plaything in the laboratory, with which it was possible to produce some almost magic-seeming results. The word "electricity" is derived from the Greek word *elektron,* their name for amber. For many centuries it had been known that when amber was rubbed hard it possessed the property of attracting to itself light particles of matter, just as we can rub the back of a comb briskly against a piece of cloth and then pick up small fragments of tissue paper with the static electricity thus produced.

Others before Faraday's time had devised chemical cells for supplying continuous electric current, and had also proved that there was some close connection between magnetism and electricity. But it was he who decided that if it was possible to produce magnetism from electricity, it should also be feasible to reverse the process and convert magnetism into an electric current. It says much for his tenacity of purpose that it took him the ten years from 1821 to 1831 to produce a solution to the problem.

It was in 1821 that Faraday made the first machine to be driven by electric power. It was nothing like our modern electric motor, of course, but it was to be the foundation of the motive force behind so much of our modern machinery and domestic appliances.

Having succeeded in harnessing electricity at this elementary level, he found it much more difficult to make a machine produce electricity. Finally, after continuous experiment, he discovered that when he thrust

MICHAEL FARADAY (1791-1867)

a magnet into a coil of wire he obtained movement in an indicating needle. A similar movement was recorded when he withdrew the magnet. The secret which had been so hard to come upon was finally his. He now knew that moving magnetism was necessary for the production of electricity.

And so we have the initial knowledge which gave us the means of producing our modern power: the dynamo. Faraday was to bequeath to us this means of producing the most widely used force of lighting, heating, and power that we have today.

Completely new industries were to arise from his discoveries. Our cities were to be brighter and cleaner. Our toil was to be less arduous, both in the home and in the factory. His genius made possible the minute spark for our internal combustion engines, and the huge dynamos at work in our power stations, our electric telegraph and the telephone, and the countless uses to which our civilized world now puts electricity.

But Michael Faraday's genius did not end with his experiments in electricity and electromagnetism. Together with Davy, his experiments with chlorine proved of untold use to our textile trade. He experimented successfully in the creation of steel alloys, acoustics and optics, and the various applications of induced electricity are but a few of the findings of this truly remarkable man.

He always remembered his own humble beginnings and in his private life was modest and self-effacing. As a lecturer at the Royal Institution he converted the jargon of the scientist into the everyday language of the layman. His lectures and experiments were calculated to inspire the generation following him to carry further the work he had begun.

When he died peacefully in his study chair at Hampton Court, 1867, he was deeply mourned. The London errand boy had become a world-famous personality.

It was in all sincerity that Sir Humphry Davy said, when congratulated on his achievements: "My best discovery — was Michael Faraday."

## EXPERIMENTS

### INDUCED ELECTRICITY

THE Greeks discovered that when substances such as amber were rubbed with cloth they became electrically charged. Many substances lose their electric charge almost as soon as it is induced, for example iron, copper, and these are called *conductors* of electricity. But amber, ebonite, plastic, polythene,

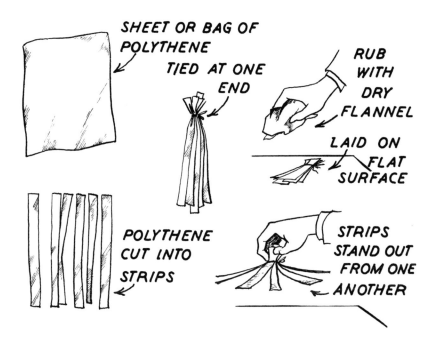

SHEET OR BAG OF POLYTHENE

TIED AT ONE END

RUB WITH DRY FLANNEL

LAID ON FLAT SURFACE

POLYTHENE CUT INTO STRIPS

STRIPS STAND OUT FROM ONE ANOTHER

etc., retain their induced charge on the surface for some time. These latter substances are called *insulators*.

Substances which become charged with electricity when rubbed may either carry an induced positive or negative electric charge. When substances with similar electric charges, i.e. both negative or both positive, are brought close together they will repel each other.

For our first experiment in Michael Faraday's lead, we will

induce an electric charge in strips of polythene. As all the strips will carry the same sort of charge they will repel each other so that they stand out separately.

The experiment shows how electric energy can be induced by friction.

You will need: Polythene; thread; piece of flannel.

Cut a sheet or bag of polythene into narrow strips. Tie these strips at one end. Place them on a flat surface and rub them with even strokes of a piece of dry flannel, from the tied ends to the free ends. After ten or twelve strokes with the flannel raise the polythene. The induced charge of electricity will cause the strips to stand out from each other (see diagram).

### MAKING AN ELECTRIC MOTOR

When an electric current is passed around a wire coil, the coil acts like a magnet. One end of the coil becomes a north pole and the other end becomes a south pole.

If like poles (i.e., the two north poles or the two south poles) are brought together, they repel each other. When unlike poles (a north and a south) are brought together, they attract each other. These are the simple facts used in making any electric motor.

Faraday changed moving energy into electrical energy when he made the first dynamo. Using the knowledge that he discovered, we are going to do the opposite and change electrical energy into moving energy by means of a simple electric motor.

You will need: A wooden base (plywood or hardwood); two strips of tin; two screws; a plastic knitting needle; a large cork; a quantity of thin cotton-covered wire; a 6-volt battery; two permanent bar magnets.

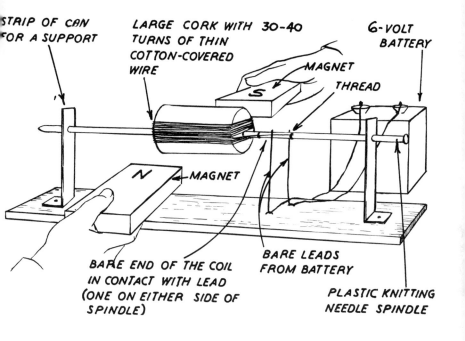

STRIP OF CAN FOR A SUPPORT

LARGE CORK WITH 30-40 TURNS OF THIN COTTON-COVERED WIRE

6-VOLT BATTERY

MAGNET

THREAD

S

N — MAGNET

BARE END OF THE COIL IN CONTACT WITH LEAD (ONE ON EITHER SIDE OF SPINDLE)

BARE LEADS FROM BATTERY

PLASTIC KNITTING NEEDLE SPINDLE

The two strips of tin should have a hole punched into each end. At one end, these holes should be large enough to allow the knitting needle to turn freely. The holes at the opposite ends of the strips should be large enough to receive small screws with which the tin supports may be secured to the baseboard.

Bore a hole through the center of the cork. Insert the knitting needle. Make 30 or 40 turns of the cotton-covered wire around the cork, as shown in the diagram. Bared ends of the coil must be carefully secured with thread so that they are on opposite sides of the knitting needle.

Position the knitting needle in the supports and arrange two leads from the battery so that their bared ends come into direct contact with the ends of the wire from the coil.

Make sure that the knitting needle spindle revolves freely. Then position two bar magnets so that one north and one south pole are present on each side of the cork-coil. As soon as the magnets are brought close enough to exert their force on the magnetic poles induced in the coil your electric motor will start turning.

1. A current passes through the coil and makes it act like a magnet. The upper side of the cork will act as the north or south pole of a magnet (depending upon which way the current is flowing into the coil) and the lower side of the cork will become the opposite pole to the top.

2. The poles of the cork-coil magnet will be attracted to the opposite poles of the permanent magnets and the cork will turn so that poles of the coil magnet will face these opposite poles; but in so doing the electric contact will be broken and current will stop flowing.

3. However, the speed at which the cork turns carries it past the poles of the outside magnets and, once more, contact is remade with the battery. This time, the bottom of the cork-coil is facing upward and vice versa, and so what was the north pole of the coil now becomes the south pole and the south becomes the north.

4. Once again the coil's magnetic poles will be attracted to the permanent magnetic poles and the cork will turn once more. This movement will persist as long as a current flows around the coil and the permanent magnets are kept in place.

# INDEX

# FAMOUS PHYSICISTS

# INDEX

10.00

**920**    **Mann, A. L.**
**M**       **Famous physicists**

Short biographies of Archimedes, Roger Bacon, Galileo, Otto von Guericke, Sir Isaac Newton, Benjamin Franklin, Luigi Galvani, Alessandro Volta, and Michael Faraday.

B 17-383